M'COBEN, PLACE OF GHOSTS

M'COBEN, PLACE OF GHOSTS

by Alice Peterson

With Best Wishes,

Alice

Witchingham Press

Published in Great Britain in 2003
by Witchingham Press, 12 Kensington Park Mews, London W11 2EY
Telephone 020 7792 6899

British Cataloguing-in-Publication Data
A catalogue record for this book is available from the British Library

ISBN 0-9545920-0-X

Designed and typeset by Perfect World Communications, London
Printed and bound in Great Britain by St Edmundsbury Press,
Bury-St-Edmunds, Suffolk

ACKNOWLEDGEMENTS

There are many people I would like to thank. Firstly, Aunt Diana, who kept the hundreds of letters written by Granny to her mother, so neatly tied together, highlighting the subject of each – and who told me of a clever numbering system so as not to find the letters in an irreversibly chaotic muddle. You have helped so much with the book. By giving me intimate details of family and backgrounds to stories, along with letting me use descriptions from the diary you wrote when we travelled to Zimbabwe, you have made the script more colourful and dynamic.

While writing *M'Coben, Place of Ghosts*, I have built up a wonderful relationship with freelance editor Anna Powell. She has encouraged, inspired, advised and passionately worked on the script with me.

To Antony Smith and Eleanor Smith for backing *M'Coben, Place of Ghosts*. I am so grateful to you.

To lovely Helen for her creativity, enthusiasm and support in the project.

Mum and Dad. Thank you for always believing in me. You are the best.

Thank you Granny, above all, for sharing your story.

Also by Alice Peterson

A WILL TO WIN

Praise for *A Will to Win*

'This true story of determination and courage cannot fail to move readers.' *OK Magazine*

'Peterson's book chronicles not only her physical decline, but also the overwhelming psychological tsunami faced by someone with a degenerative disease.' *The Times*

'Alice Peterson's startling account of her attempts to come to terms with a degenerative disease is both inspiring and accomplished...This frank account will dispel a lot of the stereotypes associated with RA and gives testament to the strength and love of a family that was unwilling to be defeated. At times funny and forthright this astonishing account by a local woman will be a source of inspiration to all those who read it.' *Winchester & Bishops Waltham Observer*

'An engrossing book... deeply affecting.' *Arthritis Today*

'The book is funny, entertaining and fast-paced, with a mercilessly-close observation of everyone from the coaches at the tennis club to the officials on the courts. It is so immediate that you feel you are in the car with the teenage whirlwind and her Mum, Pam, as they follow the British tournament circuit.'
Hampshire Chronicle

'It's a compulsive read and as honest and engaging as Alice herself.' The University of Bristol, *Nonesuch Magazine*

FOR GRANNY

CHAPTER ONE

Church of St James, Chipping Campden,
Friday 4 October 2002.
Service in Memory of Margaret Barry,
26 June 1903 – 17 September 2002.

We all piled into the coach. It reminded me of my school days. We had just eaten lunch outside, the sky was a cloudless bright blue and the sun warmed our faces. Everyone's spirits were high. Today was a celebration of our grandmother's life. My mother's mother. She died at the age of ninety-nine.

Great urns of white lilies filled the church with a wonderful scent; Bach's Prelude and Fugue in B Minor played in the background. The pews were already packed. Mum was talking to Bill Anderson, with his wife and daughters. When Granny lived in Africa after the war she became involved in the Fairbridge Farm Schools project. A school was opened for boys in Rhodesia. I remembered Granny telling me she more-or-less adopted Bill and his brother. They were orphaned children from Scotland who spent each school holiday at Granny's home.

Emma, Aunt Anne's daughter and my eldest first cousin, was on the opposite side of the church, with her husband and two sons. As always, she was dressed in beautiful bright colours. Granny had twenty grandchildren and thirty-two great-grandchildren. My sister Helen's daughter Emy was her youngest great-grandchild. Helen brought her to the service because she wanted to be able to tell her that she had been to her great-grandmother's funeral. As more cousins with their families filed into the church I had this extraordinary feeling that each one of us was connected to Granny. Had it not been for her, none of us would be here now. She has left this great legacy behind her.

I gripped the funeral service sheet. As the youngest of her grandchildren, I had been asked to do a reading and felt nervous because I wanted to do it justice. Uncle Peregrine was giving the address. He must have been feeling anxious too.

As I sat quietly I thought about the first time I stayed alone with Granny. I was seven. The family deposited me in Gloucestershire while they swanned off to Wales for a swimming and tennis holiday. I had been outraged. 'What am I going to do with Granny?' I wailed. In fact, I had a lovely time. For the last twenty years of her life Granny lived in Mickleton, a small village near Chipping Campden. Here she was close to her daughter Patricia, and Patricia's husband Peregrine. Her house was called 'The Flower Garden', a small, pretty red brick cottage – I always picture it on a beautiful summer's day, the roses surrounding the front door, and Granny peering through the window, waiting for the sound of our car's engine.

During that first visit, I will never forget Granny and I setting off for a shopping trip to Stratford. We climbed on to the rickety bus at Mickleton. After forty minutes we were both getting restless and the long narrow country roads seemed endless. 'Are we nearly there?' I asked her repeatedly. Granny agreed that we did seem to be driving around in circles so she asked the conductor if we were on the right bus. He assured us that we were indeed heading towards Stratford.

We then spotted a sign which read, 'Mickleton, two miles'. 'We must be collecting everyone in the neighbouring villages,' Granny said out loud. We laughed and laughed. Granny had this wicked, infectious cackle, which I can hear now.

From then on Granny became a good friend. When I was at school I gave a talk for an English class describing how Granny was the daughter of the 6th Earl of Radnor and brought up in a castle, and then she and my grandfather, Gerald, set up a home and farm in the wilds of Africa. The main focus of the talk was snakes. I told the gory story of Mum and Granny being attacked by a black mamba when out riding. 'Mum's twin brother, Richard, shot the black mamba's head off with the only bullet left in the gun,' I relayed with pride.

At twelve I started to play tennis competitively. When Granny was doing her 'royal tour,' of all her children, she often came to watch. Her eyesight was beginning to fail her and a host of 'bad luck darling's flew out when I had just hit a winning shot. But it was only when I was diagnosed with rheumatoid arthritis (RA) at the age of eighteen that Granny became a central figure in my life. I spent a lot of time at home being looked after by my parents – not something I would have wished for, but it did mean that when Granny came to stay I really got to know her. I knew how she liked her orange cut into neat segments in the morning with her brown bread and honey. She loved going to Sainsbury's with Mum and buying us dark chocolate and sherry. She was a wonderful support to us. I remember her rubbing her frail hands gently over mine, saying she wished she could take away the pain. Her skin was paper-thin and her fingers felt soft like melting butter. When we went upstairs to bed she would kiss me on the landing and hug me tightly. I often try to remember her touch, the way it felt.

Aunt Diana, Mum and I visited Granny's home, M'Coben, in Zimbabwe, in January 2000. When my grandparents bought their farmland they discovered that M'Coben meant 'Place of Ghosts'. They loved the name and decided to keep it. Today, the name seems all the more appropriate. For Zimbabwe the Millennium was the year of the infamous Land Grab, when murder and mayhem was the norm on many farms carried out by so-called War Veterans and supported by Government soldiers and the police.

I looked at Aunt Diana who was sitting in front of us – children and grandchildren sitting alongside her. She turned and smiled and I knew we were thinking the same. How lucky we had been to see Granny's home before it was too late. The travelling was tough at times because I had just had an operation on my ankle, but I felt overwhelmingly glad to have gone. The many conversations I had had with Granny, sitting on the sofa-bed recording her stories, came to life. Being in Africa and sitting at Granny's desk where she wrote her letters home to her mother, brought me closer to her memories.

Uncle Peregrine walked up to the lectern, standing tall and distinguished. He climbed the four narrow steps and settled his papers. He looked ahead, and then began:

'Margaret, in whose memory we come here today with gratitude, affection and love, asked us in her Will not to mourn her, so this is a happy occasion.

After Gerald's death Margaret lived with memories of an

exceptionally happy marriage and with the confident certainty that she would join him again at her death. We can be certain that, in whatever form the afterlife may be, she is having a lovely time with him now making sure he has supplies of cherry cake, whisky and cigars while she tells him what happened during the last twenty-five years.

Her life was governed by three things: her love for Gerald and her family, her faith as a Christian, and her great zest for everything.

Gerald died a quarter of a century ago and Margaret told Marcus[1] that she had thought about him every morning since. It's impossible not to think of them together. Their happiness in each other was obvious and the climate they created together for their children was one of happy affection and support punctuated when necessary by fierce rebuke or criticism, and sometimes with a few whacks of a gym shoe.

As a child Margaret went every morning with her brothers and sisters to her mother's bedroom to say her prayers. She said them every day throughout her life, and whenever possible she went to church every Sunday, walking to church in Mickleton in her late nineties.

Her sense of duty led her to be active in the affairs of every community she found herself in. In New York during the War, as well as running a household of seventeen children, she commuted to New York City to a full-time job with the British Voluntary Movement. In Africa her community was a large one. There, after the War, she became National Chairman of the Southern Rhodesian Women's Institute and this was no sinecure. She made a point of visiting every WI throughout a country three times the size of England, driving by herself.

---

[1] Peregrine's son

Back in England she became a very active President of the Norfolk WI.

For four years of the Second World War she didn't see Gerald at all. It is difficult to imagine what those years must have been like for her, sometimes not knowing where he was or even if he were alive.

It was of course easier for the children because they were so young. When Gerald left to go to the war Patricia was seven and the twins were only midgets. When he came back Patricia went with Diana to meet his train. She couldn't remember what he looked like. So Diana said: 'Don't worry. Just kiss the one I kiss.'

I may have given the impression that she was a rather severe and aloof person. Far from it. She had a splendid sense of humour and a great sense of fun. She had a talent for summing people up accurately with devastating one-liners. We will always remember the great squawk and cackle of her laugh and its sometimes startling volume.

Children were transfixed when she read to them, leaning forward in her chair, her voice becoming an excited, breathless whisper when she got to the frightening bits about the tigers in *Little Black Sambo*; and especially about *Baba Yaga the Bony-Legged, The Witch*, gnashing her iron teeth and chasing her little niece through the forest.

I remember her at Longford not many years ago, eager as a child again showing us the place on the stairs where she was terrified a bear would leap out on her as she went up to bed; and the bath in which the nursery coal was kept.

All her children can remember how formidable her temper could be. Pam remembers an occasion when, thoroughly

aroused by some incompetence, she crowned the offender with a large tin of Nescafe.

She was never idle, a characteristic inherited, with many others, by her children. One thing, however, she mercifully did not pass on to them was her dreadful cooking. Her method entailed the keeping of every scrap of food of whatever kind. These ended up later in undiagnosable stews, nourishing perhaps but largely inedible. Alexander Aberdeen[1] was once asked by Margaret if he was enjoying his soup. 'No, it tastes like gravy,' he said.

Diana remembers the occasion when her mother and all the children, save for Anne, were about to leave their house in Aberdeen to catch a train to London on the first leg of their return journey to Africa. All their possessions had been sunk when crossing the Atlantic and they had nothing but innumerable cardboard boxes to carry. Diana said, 'Ma, shall I call the taxis?'

'Taxis,' said Margaret. 'Of course not. We'll go by tram.' The large party set off like a string of refugees.

I met her when she was forty-nine – amazingly, that was fifty years ago – but I only got to know her when she came to live in Mickleton. By then she could no longer drive because she had inner ear trouble, but she could certainly walk. Until her mid-nineties she would often walk alone up the steep hill to Kiftsgate and back.

Every Sunday she walked at least a mile and a half at Norton. During her visits with Patricia and me to North Uist in the Hebrides, she would walk, every day, a three-mile circuit of tidal flats, shingle, shore and machair. She walked at such a speed that in the township of Balranald she was

---

[1] Anne's son

7

universally known as Lady Jackie Stewart.

As she got frailer, she slowed down and eventually, when walking, needed some support but her hand was like a butterfly on your arm.

When walking outside became difficult for her, she would have an afternoon nap in the sitting room. 'What music would you like Margaret?'

'Mottzzart,' she would reply firmly.

At weekends she would be waiting punctually to be collected from her house in Mickleton: always such a smart figure, her hair done and wearing one of her ancient dresses that somehow looked up-to-date, and always wearing the brooch that Gerald had given her; knowing the Test score and who had made runs or taken wickets, whether Steve Davis, her favourite because he had such good manners, was beating Jimmy White at The Crucible.

When she could no longer see she would ask what we were eating for lunch or dinner and whatever Patricia told her, she would invariably say, 'How delicious darling.' I think she would have said the same if Patricia had said 'iron fillings'.

She had an appetite like a horse and when asked if she would like some more she would answer, 'I have had quite sufficient, a lovely meal thank you.'

'Are you sure?' Patricia would say.

'Well perhaps just a little more,' and she would pack away a substantial second helping.

As she grew frailer she became a little deaf but she dealt brilliantly even with this affliction. She listened carefully to what was said and then would say either, 'Really' or 'What a shame' and usually got away with it.

She waited eagerly for telephone calls from and about her family – they were her meat and drink but she never complained if she was neglected. She knew the birth dates of every one of her vast family and her only extravagances were the fivers and book tokens she sent to her grandchildren.

She bore all her sadnesses with courage: the loss of her precious Gill, the death of Gerald, terrible burns on her hands followed by weeks of painful skin grafts, her blindness and increasing frailty.

She grew old graciously and gallantly. Until the very last twilight months of her life her interest in everything and everybody never flagged and, until the end, she kept her dignity and her standards.

Goodness is hard to define yet we recognise it instinctively and it was there in her. She represented everything that commands respect in her generation. The example she gave to her children, grandchildren and her thirty-two great-grandchildren showed them constantly qualities which we have all but lost in our present raucous, mannerless and violent age.

She had nobility of spirit. We were lucky to have her with us for so long.'

CHAPTER TWO

Longford Castle, Salisbury
August, 1999

We drive through imposing wrought-iron gates and pass a wooded area running alongside a chalk stream. The road curves sharply round to the right. As I lean out of the window, looking across Longford Park, I can see in the distance a magnificent castle built of pale grey stone and flint. The driveway straightens out to the approach of what looks like a fairytale castle, with beautiful surrounding parkland, well tended paddocks and a small golf course for staff. Mum tells me that Longford was bought by Granny's ancestors, the Bouverie family, in 1717. I have visited Longford only once, when I was six. It is much larger than I remembered.

This was where Granny grew up. Her home.

The Radnor flag, a demi-eagle with two heads, is flying in the centre between the three round towers. 'The original house was built in 1592, in a triangle with a tower at each point to represent the Trinity,' Granny explains.

The gravel drive sweeps into a large semi-circle in front of the castle.

Jake and Jill Radnor greet us at the front door. The butler smiles and takes our coats. Jake Radnor is Granny's nephew, her brother William's eldest son. Granny told me she took Jake to America during the Second World War, along with William's four other children, her own family of six and her brother Barty's two.

'This used to be our central hall,' Granny begins proudly. Her pace quickens as she walks confidently across the large triangular hall past a hobby horse. There are stone spiral staircases at each point of the triangle. 'There was a piano, a sofa, lots of chairs and a big table for the post.' As she remembers she indicates with her head where everything used to be. It is like watching Granny step into the past. She sees her home as she remembered it ninety years ago. Can I step back into the past with her?

Granny marches on to the 'round parlour'. It is a lovely room, in one of the towers, with gold and white panelled walls. Fresh orchids from the glass houses sit on a table. 'This was my mother's 'boudoir', where she wrote her business letters, did her sewing or read.'

'Granny, would this have been where your mother wrote her weekly letter to you when you were out in Africa?'

'Yes, exactly. I am sure she would have read my letters in here too,' she says.

Granny sits down and takes a full glass of champagne from a tray being passed around by the butler. 'Mother taught all her ten children to read and write in here. It was quite unusual, Alice, for a lady to teach her own children. I can see even now the print of her beautifully written copies that she did herself for us.'

1907

Barty, Margaret and Anty sat around the small square table with their heads down and sharpened pencils in their hands.

'Pot hooks and hangers,' Margaret copied carefully under the rounded letters. Her mouth felt dry. She could still taste the piece of chocolate she had been given after the kitchen visit. 'Coats, shoes and buttons,' she continued happily. Next it was the arithmetic which she did not enjoy quite so much, although she did not dare say so. She suddenly felt a prod under the table. 'Marka!' Barty whispered, pointing down to his three completed sentences. 'I want to be promoted to the school room.'

'Well you know you can't be until we have read *Little Arthur's History of England*,' Margaret replied. 'Right through,' she added.

Mother peered over her book, *Reading without Tears*. Heads immediately went down again.

We are now on the second floor of the castle. Granny and I walk down the long corridors. Although she walks slowly there is a certain urgency to her stride. Her footsteps stamp authority and I would not dare to walk in front of her. 'This is the bedroom I slept in when I was seventeen and had returned from France. I had been sent to Ozannes' finishing school in 1920.'

'What was that like?'

'Well, it was rather lovely. I loved Paris. My flat over-looked the Eiffel Tower and we were taken to museums. I saw the Mona Lisa, you know, but I wasn't so keen on the Impressionists. The school was run by three sisters, sisters d'Ozanne. One of them was frightening. When my cousin, Duncan Balfour, turned up wanting to take me out to the theatre and on to dinner she would not allow this until she received confirmation from my mother that he was my cousin,' she tells me.

'Well I hope she felt a real fool when she discovered that he was your cousin?'

'She must have done. We had a wonderful time. He took me to a musical. I also learnt to cook in France. We didn't learn anything much, but we were photographed during one lesson and an article was printed in the *Illustrated London News*. They were interested in titled ladies learning cooking in France.'

'How funny, Granny.' I try not to laugh at this idea as I look out of the window to the garden.

'Well, yes, I suppose it was,' she says. 'We cooked nothing fancy.'

Granny stands by me and seems to follow my gaze. 'We used to play in the formal gardens, darting in between the yew hedges. We used to go bathing in the river too. We had rowing boats, canoes, a punt and a sailing dinghy.' Her mind is like a picture book, she only has to turn the pages to see it all.

She shows us all the adjoining rooms. Granny had four sisters and five brothers, so I find it astonishing that her memory can guide her to exactly who slept where. 'This is Kitty's bedroom, and next door Jeane's, and this is Willie's bedroom. I used to call him Billum,' she says fondly. Then adds enviously, 'He had a four poster bed.'

'The bedrooms are gorgeous, Granny,' I say, touching one of the curtains with its elaborate trim.

'Yes, I'm sure they are now. Ours weren't particularly special, we always had old wallpaper and dud curtains.' Granny walks into the next room. 'Come here! Alice! Keep up!'

We are now standing in the doorway to her mother's bedroom, one of the round tower rooms, where Granny was born on 26 June, 1903. Her mother, Julian, the Countess of Radnor had ten children – Granny was her seventh.

'I must tell you, when we were born there was no telephone in the house. The pony and trap waited fully harnessed in the stables, ready when word came from the house to fetch the doctor three miles in from Salisbury.'

The Countess of Radnor held the tiny baby in her arms. She stroked its dark hair. She was overjoyed to have a baby girl as her last two children had been boys. 'I would like to call her Margaret,' she said, looking at her husband.

'I think that's a fine name,' he agreed. 'Let us call her Marka for short.'

At the end of the month, the maternity nurse was ready to hand Margaret over to Nanny and nursery-care. Nanny, the head nurse, had been on holiday and was unaware of the latest arrival to the family. The groom in charge of the carriage met her at the station with a wide smile. 'Her Ladyship has had a beautiful baby girl,' he told her.

'I can't believe I was beautiful,' Granny exclaims. 'I don't think babies are. I suppose it was a way of confirming that I was sound in wind and limb. We used always to come into mother's room in the morning to say our prayers,' she continues. 'Mother had a hip bath although they had a large bathroom which only father used. Do you know, I think it was the only bathroom in the house. Tell me what's in this room now.' I turn to look at Granny. Sometimes I forget that she cannot see, it's only her questions which remind me. Isn't it incredible that a blind person can still hold so much life in their eyes?

Three circular stone staircases lead up from the points of the triangle forming the central hall, one of which is the uncarpeted staircase the children used, taking you up to the nurseries. Two nightlights used to light the stairs, one at the bottom and one at the top. 'It was terrifying running up the stone stairs in the dark to join the nursery party at bedtime,' Granny shivers as if she can feel the coldness beneath her feet, 'I was frightened of the dark spooky passages with their eerie shadows. I used to think a bear might come after me. My mother and father had their own staircase, which we've already walked past. Theirs was carpeted, leading to their bedroom floor, the billiard room, and the picture gallery.'

The Day Nursery is another round tower room, still filled with toys and the little brick and white coloured house which Granny and her brothers and sisters played in. The original wallpaper was pink, with Chinese figures and birds and butterflies pasted on painstakingly by their great-aunts. 'Until I was seven I lived my life in this nursery,' Granny reflects. 'All our meals were brought up here, often cold by the time they arrived. We used to make toast at the nursery fire.'

Margaret climbed into the rocking boat, while her little sister, Helen, was helped on to the rocking horse. Nanny Liza, attired in her high-necked white dress with a gathered up piece of embroidery on her head, sat at the round table with the nursery staff. They were surrounded by needles, buttons, cotton and lace. Liza was making Margaret and Helen's petticoats and knickers. She looked over to Margaret who was now on the rocking horse, her favourite toy. She was growing up quickly and needed another white smocked dress too. The children were not allowed to go downstairs in their day clothes. They had to wear pretty white dresses with ribbons.

A white cloth now covered the table ready for lunch.

Margaret peered into the pot, disheartened to see it was Irish stew again. None of them liked Irish stew. It was always cold by the time it had travelled from the kitchen to the nursery. As she put a small chunk into her mouth she could feel the cold mutton fat sticking to the roof of her mouth.

'I did love that rocking horse,' Granny smiles. 'I longed to learn to ride properly.'

I walk over to the window and ask Granny where the stables were.

'To the right of the house, tucked around the back. When we were little, the nursery party used to be taken out for a drive in the wagonette.'

Margaret frowned as she saw the familiar sight of the open wagonette drawing up at the front door. As the children assembled outside, Leonard, the stable boy, jumped off the box and ran to the back of the carriage. He opened the door and stood very still as the children clambered in. Margaret liked Leonard's top hat but his plum-coloured frock coat was falling off his shoulders. He held the baby while Nanny stepped in. 'Mind you don't drop him, young man,' she said.

The wagonette took them up on the downs. Trip trot, trip trot. Barty and Margaret's legs were sitting in a double woollen bag to keep them warm. They spent the entire journey kicking each other. 'I spy with my little eye something beginning with F H,' Barty started.

'Fred's horses,' Margaret guessed lethargically. Fred was the coachman. She kicked Barty again, 'Where is Anty?'

'Anty was hiding in the boiler room. I wish I had been as clever,' Granny hoots with laughter.

'I would have loved to travel like that instead of driving in boring old cars,' I sigh, 'or being shoved on to the back of Mum's bicycle.'

'I'm ashamed that I thought it was so boring.'

I am now dead on my feet and my ankle is aching, but we continue walking past more bedrooms – bedrooms where Granny slept in the winter, musty bedrooms where Granny slept in the summer, the French governess' room. 'There was no gas or electric lighting when I was little,' Granny explains. 'Carrying candles stood by every bedside.' If I was on my own, I'd need an A-Z of the house, or chalk to mark the walls, showing I'd been there. I cannot imagine living here. It's too big. I would need roller-skates to get around.

We come to a blocked off passage to the tower where Granny used to have her school lessons. 'We had a dreadful governess, she used to keep me behind after lessons to test me on my spelling. Anty once hurled an ink pot at her!' she beams with triumph.

'Serves her right!'

'Yes, quite.'

'Did you ever do anything naughty when you were little?'

'No, never.' Granny shakes her head.

'You must have done!'

I can draw up a long list of my pranks. I used to defrost the fridge when Mum had dinner parties. I particularly remember one time when she went into the kitchen, ready to impress her guests with the pudding, opened the fridge and shrieked when she saw her strawberry mousses floating on the bottom shelf. I was nicknamed 'The Pill' – defrosting the fridge was only the tip of a very large iceberg.

Granny and I cram into the lift. It's 4pm. I know this because Granny's special watch for the blind has just quacked the time at me. When you press one of the buttons it tells you the time, 'It is 7.15pm,' it quacks loudly, occasionally followed by an unexplained cock-a-doodle-do.

We descend one floor to the chapel bedrooms. Granny marches ahead but I am desperately thirsty so slip into the next room and drink out of the bottle of water that sits next to the bed. I feel if I lay down I might wake up seventy years earlier when Granny was my age. I close my eyes and try to imagine it.

'Alice, where are you?' Granny's asking, already standing at the next room. 'The saloon is down there,' she points with her white stick, 'where we had our dances. It had great big pictures in it. I must tell you how much my parents entertained. The house was always full of people. Barty, Anty, Ned and I used to sit in the dark gallery overlooking the hall and watch the parties going on. It was like watching a play.'

Margaret sat close to Barty and pulled her dressing gown cord tightly around her waist without looking away from the guests. She pulled a strand of hair away from her eyes. Nanny insisted on putting curl-rags in her hair at night so that she

18

woke up with perfect ringlets. It bored Margaret stiff having her hair done and Nanny could tell. 'Il faut souffrir, pour être belle,' she told Margaret whenever she saw a glimpse of a frown or impatience. Margaret gazed at the glittering jewels and silks of the ladies' dresses, sparkling under the candlelight.

Mr Warman threw open the big double doors. Margaret's heart sank. Why couldn't he be late, just for once? She didn't want to go to bed yet. Mr Warman was their butler. One of his duties was to ring the gong in the hallway half an hour before dinner and then five minutes before. He was strict and solemn-faced. She was a little scared of him. 'Here he comes,' Margaret sighed, knowing the show was nearly over.

'Dinner is served, m'lord,' he announced pompously. He then dramatically turned on his feet, went back through the doors and down to the dining room.

Margaret watched her father take the arm of a tall slim lady. Her golden-coloured hair was fastened back with diamond clips and she was wearing matching diamond drop earrings. Her shimmering gold low-cut silk dress seemed to glide with each step she made. Margaret thought she looked like a princess. 'Perhaps she is a princess,' she whispered to Barty, her eyes wide with awe.

'I think the lady on Lord Cecil Manners arm looks the loveliest,' whispered Nanny to Elsie England, one of the nursery maids. Margaret turned round to see the lady's maids and the nannies straining their necks over the balustrade.

'No, no, Miss Kitty Stafford looks much better,' insisted Elsie. 'She's on the arm of Colonel Wingfield. Haven't you seen the ruby necklace she is wearing?'

'I think Miss Stafford's dress is rather plain,' Nanny huffed.

Two by two they started to disappear through the doors. Margaret gazed longingly at her mother's blue full-length gown. She was wearing the family tiara like she always did. She had once shown it to Margaret. Margaret had tentatively touched one of the diamonds and then withdrew her hand immediately, scared by its beauty. Mother was standing at the back with her partner. She was always the last to go which Margaret thought unfair.

When the hall was quiet Nanny hurried the children upstairs. Nanny tucked her into bed, folding the blanket over her long-sleeved white night dress with embroidered edging. Margaret closed her eyes and dreamed of wearing that gold dress to the first dinner and dance she would go to, holding on to the arm of a tall dark handsome man.

The castle is strangely quiet, all I can hear is the click of my shoes. I turn to her. 'Do you miss Longford?'

'Yes,' she nods gently. 'It was one of the hardest things I've ever had to do, leaving my family and home. I did it for Gerald. It was an awful break for me. You see, I was thousands of miles apart from my family with no means of getting in touch with them. Communication was so primitive, Alice. I lost all my friends and hated being away from my family. But I wanted to be with him. I would have followed him wherever he chose to go.'

As I listen to Granny, I realise how much I admire her for going overseas, where life was going to change in every possible way. She has lived through two world wars and witnessed more social change than we are ever likely to. Theirs is a fading generation. But what is so unusual about her story is that she has lived two lives of such great contrast. Her mother had a Hepplewhite bureau in her boudoir. Granny glowed with pride when she told me Gerald made her a bedside table out of a petrol box for their bedroom at M'Coben. Longford was landscaped by Capability Brown. Granny reared her children in wild African veldt. As I stand here, it's hard to believe Granny saying that when she was in Africa she had to sell her old stockings to make a bit of money because they were poor. Yet she was happy because she was with Gerald. She would have sacrificed anything to be with him.

Granny is ninety-six. How much time do I have to hear her story before it is too late?

'I would love to write your story,' I tell her. 'I want to go to Africa and when I come home I will describe everything to you. It will seem like you have been back. You'll be with us.'

Granny smiles as she clutches on to my arm and says, 'I would love that.'

I don't want ever to say I never really knew my grandmother.

CHAPTER THREE

Granny is lying down on the sofa-bed in our sitting room. Her arms are crossed. She's wearing a pretty pink shirt with a matching cardigan. I can't think how she manages to choose her clothes. They always match perfectly. Only occasionally she gets muddled over the colour of her tights. When she comes to stay Mum asks her if she needs a hand dressing. 'No, I can do it,' she says politely.

'Are you ready?' I ask her.

'Yes,' she replies, crossing her legs too.

I switch on the dictaphone. 'I want to hear about Grandpa. When did you become interested in boys, Granny?' It feels strange asking her this. She has a blue checked rug pulled over her lap, an old pair of glasses perched on her powdered nose and she is now clicking her false teeth back into position. I panic. Can I really translate Granny with her clacking false teeth and her cock-a-doodle-do watch into a vibrantly real young woman? Try to imagine her as a young girl, I tell myself. I have seen old photographs of her and she was very pretty. She had lovely soft dark brown hair with red highlights and blue eyes. She also had a rather determined chin. 'The only person who has a longer chin than me is Granny,' Mum always jokes.

'When I was seventeen I started going to the dances. My parents gave me a "coming out" dance at Longford in January, 1921, before I went to London to start "the season".'

'How lovely.'

'Well, it wasn't,' she says matter-of-factly. 'I had an

ingrown toenail. I was terribly disappointed as I had a new white satin ball gown especially for the occasion. I could not glide down the staircase or dance. All I could do was hobble on my sticks.'

'How miserable.'

'I was miserable by the end of the evening. Very tearful by bedtime. After that I stayed with Mary Thynne in London. She was the daughter of Lady Bath. They had a large London house on the west side of Grosvenor Square. We went to a dance every night.'

'Every night! What a party girl!'

'Yes, I was,' she smiles proudly.

'Before we talk about the dances, I can't wait to hear more about the first time you met Gerald.' I didn't know my grand-father. All I know is that he was a wonderful fisherman. Granny once showed me a carving of a fish that had been modelled on a salmon Gerald had caught in the River Spey. It was so enormous I thought it was a shark. 'What did you talk about?'

'All sorts of things. He was in the Coldstream Guards. He told me that if he gave up the army he would like to be an architect. I talked to him about my time in France. I went to a finishing school to "grow up" as my mother put it. I remember thinking how mature Gerald was for his age. He was twenty-four.'

'The war must have matured him,' I suggest.

'Yes, that's right,' she agrees, 'to see such terrible things at a young age must have made him grow up into a man overnight.'

'Did he talk to you about the war?'

'Oh yes,' she replies, as if it would have been totally natural to talk about it. I had always heard it was a forbidden subject, the men wanting to forget as well as protect the women from the truth. I wonder whether it was unusual for him to talk in this way?

'When you met for the first time, did it feel like you had known each other for years?' I ask Granny hopefully. 'Did you know that he was "the one"?'

'No, not really. Although we did get on ever so well.'

'Oh,' I shrug with disappointment.

February 1921

'I'm sitting next to that oily man Desmond,' Margaret whispered in dismay having caught a glimpse of the seating plan.

'Oh heavens, the little man? The banker?' Mary asked.

'Yes,' Margaret nodded with further disappointment.

'Who's on your other side?'

'Gerald Barry.'

'Oh, now he's Lady Mildred Fitzgerald's nephew. Don't you think he's rather dashing? They're standing together.'

Margaret looked over at Mildred's elegant figure with her wasp-like waist. She was standing with a tall slim man with blond hair. He *is* wonderful looking, she thought to herself. As he looked back across the room at her, Margaret turned to Mary and smiled.

'I'm Gerald Barry, how-do-you-do.' They shook hands.

'Margaret Pleydell-Bouverie.'

Gerald already knew her name. He had asked Mildred who the slim dark-haired girl was.

As lunch began, Margaret told Gerald that she had just moved to London. 'I'm living with Mary Thynne. Mary's mother knows your Aunt Mildred.'

They talked about London, Margaret saying how much she was looking forward to 'the season'.

Gerald told her that he was in the army. 'I was in France during the war,' he said. He had fudged his age, pretending he was eighteen when he was only seventeen. He was determined to fight, missing his last year at Eton. He thought that the war would be over quickly and under no condition was he going to miss being a part of it.

'I was only eleven when war broke out,' Margaret told him. Her memories of those four years were of anxiously waiting for telegrams from her brother, Ned, or her father. Her mother turned Longford into a hospital. She and her brothers used to write blood and thunder-type plays, in which the German spies were always the villains. They would perform them for the soldiers. Could she ever truly understand what Gerald had been through?

'My brother, Ned, joined the Navy as a midshipman, not yet aged fifteen,' she said. 'When HMS Hogue sank in the North Sea, Ned must have swum for about three hours before he was picked up,' she exclaimed incredulously. 'Mother received a telegram and we feared he had died. A week later, Ned arrived back at Longford and threw stones up at the footman's window. Unknown to us, he wrote a letter to Mother, went to the nursery, drank lots of milk and put himself to bed. The following morning the footman was carrying the letter on a silver salver and asked me to take it to my mother. When I saw it was in Ned's writing I yelled across the landing, "Ned's home. Ned's home."' Margaret's face reddens with the excitement of the story. It does not matter how many times she tells it, it's as vivid as if it were yesterday.

Gerald had not talked about the war, not to anyone. 'I would not have survived had I not been wounded,' he found himself saying. 'I was shot in the knee and chest. One of the doctors told me they were going to amputate. "That leg's a gonner. Take it off," he said to the other doctor in charge.'

'Oh how dreadful.' Margaret did not know what else to say.

'I overheard the second doctor reply, "But the lad's only eighteen. Give the poor boy a chance."'

'What happened then?'

'I've never had any trouble since,' Gerald smiled, patting his leg to show it was real. 'I was very fortunate.'

Gerald wanted to talk about something else. 'Do you have a large family?'

'Yes,' Margaret took in a deep breath, 'there's Jeane, Kitty, Willie, Betty, Ned,' she stopped to breathe before she reeled off the next jingle of brothers and sisters, 'Barty, me, Anty, Helen, Peter.'

Gerald laughed as he watched her intently. 'I'm surprised you remember all their names.'

'You must talk to the lady on your other side,' Margaret insisted, conscious of impatient movements from that direction. Gerald turned away reluctantly. Margaret overheard him telling the woman on his right that his barracks were in London but his home was in Norfolk. He had two sisters and a brother who was in the navy.

Gerald was trying to be polite but found himself giving the shortest of replies as he glanced sideways at Margaret. She was wearing a string of pearls and a loose-fitting silvery green dress with small delicate buttons in the same material on the shoulders. She wore a matching belt around her hips. It showed off her slim figure and the green complemented her eyes and highlighted her dark hair.

He overheard her say that her greatest passion was riding. 'My father had to teach me to ride astride otherwise I would have grown up crooked.' He listened to her claim that she could not even draw stickmen and that her brother had mistaken her picture of Ginger the horse for a sausage dog. He found himself laughing at this just as the woman to his right was telling him that her pug had died. She asked Gerald to show some sensitivity. 'I'm very sorry,' he apologised, trying to look mournful.

'How did the party end? What did Gerald say to you when he left, Granny?'

Without even thinking she says, 'We shall meet at the dances.'

'Did you tell your girlfriends how much you liked him?'

'No, no!' She pulls the blue checked rug over herself. 'We were very taken with each other, but I didn't tell anyone, not even Mary.'

'Tell me more about Mary.'

'We went to France together and I stayed with her during "the season".'

'What was she like?'

'She was tall with brown eyes.'

'But what was she like?'

'Well, she was rather beautiful, had nice clothes and a

terrific sense of humour. She was even laughing when she fell out of a taxi in a busy street in Paris. I was holding on to her legs for dear life! I think she was a little tight.'

I smile. I can't remember the last time I heard the word tight. 'You were reserved, you kept quiet about things didn't you, especially personal things? Didn't you gossip with your friends?'

'No, never. It was the way we were brought up.'

'The parties sound different from today.'

'Yes, they were. You were invited to a house party first where you were given dinner, laid on by one of the guests who lived near to the host who was giving the dance. After dinner your party was taken on to the dance. When we arrived the butler announced our names in front of the other guests. "Lady Margaret Pleydell-Bouverie," he said, and I had to shake hands with the hosts.' Granny is talking as if she was at the party now.

'Did guests kiss you on the cheek when saying hello?'

'No, no. Men never kissed you on the cheek, even if they knew you well. Gerald shook my hand, always.'

'What did you wear?'

'A lady's-maid helped me dress for the parties. I didn't have many clothes, just a few silk evening dresses and I had a lovely red velvet cloak.'

'Why didn't you have many dresses?'

'I just didn't. Mother didn't spend a lot on our clothes.'

'But you were well off, surely she could have afforded to give you lovely dresses?' I push. 'I'm only asking this Granny because there you are, living in this castle and you're saying that you didn't have many clothes. It's slightly odd.'

'Well, I didn't,' she says irritably. 'Life changed after the war. Although the hospital at Longford came to a standstill and the rooms were brought back to normal, it was never the same again.'

'What do you mean?'

'Well, perhaps we weren't as well off after my parents had put so much into turning our home into a hospital. Anyway, the war saw the end of the 'big house' way of life. Most people lived in more stringent conditions. Edwardian standards died.'

I decide not to push her any more about money. I do remember Mum saying that the Radnors were very thrifty. 'I don't like spending money on myself,' Mum says, 'or paying a lot for a meal out. I think I've inherited it from Granny's side of the family.'

'Tell me more about what you wore at the parties,' I ask.

'We wore corsets with suspenders, we didn't have tights then. We didn't have nylon or even silk stockings either, only cotton ones and we always wore long kid gloves to the dances. We had to take them to the cleaners after each dance.'

I can't think of anything worse than wearing corsets and suspenders. I couldn't be bothered squeezing my tummy into a boned framework and lacing it up tightly.

'What did the men wear?'

'Tail-coats, white shirts and white waistcoats.'

'Did you like having lady's-maids?'

'I didn't think about it, it seemed quite natural.'

'Did you wear make-up?'

'No, I didn't know a thing about it. I powdered my nose occasionally after I was married.'

I smile, picturing my dressing table overflowing with foundation creams, make-up brushes, eye-shadows, long-lash mascara, firming cream and Clarins', 'Beauty Flash Balm'.

'How did you wear your hair?'

'You had to wear it pinned up as a sign that you were grown up. I wore mine in a bun. I practised dancing in my bedroom the night before my first dance to make sure it didn't come undone!' she shrieks as she rocks forward. 'Sometimes I put hot irons in my hair to make it curl. It was quite long.'

'Were the houses you went to very smart?'

'Yes, but again I didn't think much about the pictures, the furniture, the velvet curtains, the silver and gilded cutlery. You see I'd grown up surrounded by treasures and I took it all for granted. Until I went to Africa,' she adds as an afterthought.

'Did you drink at the parties?'

'Very little. We were never given cocktails or wine before dinner. That was an innovation that came from America later on.'

'A good innovation,' I say. 'Have you ever had a hangover, Granny?' I ask.

'Have I ever had a what?' She leans forward looking confused.

'A hangover?'

'I was very tight once during the Second World War. It was a desperate time, always waiting to hear if Gerald was alive or dead. I remember my bed spinning. I drink much more now. I love my glass of sherry in the evening.'

'Don't you mean your three glasses?'

'Hum?' She leans forward again.

I decide to move on. 'Did anyone smoke?'

'No, not at the meals. Gerald smoked a pipe but never at the dinner parties.'

'Tell me more about Gerald.'

'He had very blond hair and blue eyes.'

Like thousands of other people, I want to say. Great, that gives me a really clear picture. I can see it's going to be a challenge to get buttoned up Granny to unbutton a little.

'What else?'

'He was tall and slim.'

I frown, thinking it's lucky Granny can't see my frustration.

'Tell me a story about him,' I try.

'And very good at the waltz. What did you say?'

I clear my throat. 'Tell me a story about Gerald,' I attempt again.

Silence. 'What was he like? Not in looks but in character, Granny?'

'I do remember at one dance the heel came off my shoe. He jammed it back on, covered the nail poking on the inside of the shoe with his handkerchief and we danced all night! I could never sleep after dancing with him. I used to lie awake until three in the morning, the sounds of the violin, saxophone and piano still filling the room.'

'Carry on,' I insist. 'Why did you fall in love with him?

There's another long silence. I have to pause the tape as I wait. She looks tearful. Eventually she says, 'He was the most handsome man I had ever seen. He was beautiful.'

CHAPTER FOUR

'Are you ready?' Granny asks me as she walks slowly into the room. She is so small and frail, Mum told me she weighs six and a half stone. Yet she still refuses to be given an arm for support unless absolutely necessary.

'Yes, we were talking about the dances.'

'That's right,' she says as she crosses her arms.

I slot a new tape into the machine. 'So you had to wait for someone to ask you to dance? How frightening. What happened if no one wanted to dance with you Granny?' I am imagining those awful school discos where you couldn't dance until you were asked.

'I'm afraid they were wallflowers.'

'Wallflowers?'

'Yes, girls who never got asked.'

'What did you do if you were a, "wallflower"? Where did you stand?'

'I suppose they went off to the cloakrooms to powder their noses,' she replies dismissively. 'I don't know, I never was a wallflower. I loved dancing with your grandfather. We felt so comfortable together.'

'Was Gerald romantic? Did he take you out for dinner?'

'No, we never went to restaurants, it wasn't done in those days. He was quite romantic though, he wrote me letters fairly soon after we first met.'

'What kind of things did he write?'

'"I love you", that sort of thing,' she says, far too casually.

'Already! How forward!' Hearing how easy it was for

Granny makes me envious. No games were played, it was so simple. She had her tall, devastatingly handsome man in the palm of her hand right from the beginning. I have seen pictures of Gerald and he was, as Granny says, beautiful. His features were very fine. He had a wide forehead, high cheek-bones, a thin noble jawline and penetrating blue eyes. He also had better legs than any woman deserves.

'Yes, very forward! It's not like today where you have partners for years on end. We got on with it!' She has a point there. Helen's boyfriend, James, still hasn't proposed after five years. I think she may have to start sending herself flowers and Belgian chocolates. The shell ones.

'Did you write back?'

'No, I don't remember writing back. I loved his letters. I've kept them all. He called me his "little rabbit".'

'What did you call him?'

'I just called him Gerald or "my own darling man". He was the poetic one.'

'Did you tell your mother about him?'

'No, we didn't know our parents intimately like you do.'

I would find it hard not being able to confide in my parents. I tell my mother almost everything. I don't think we would be so close if we hadn't been through the trials of the RA. When I played tennis it was Mum who drove me cross-country to play in tournaments. She maintains that there is no better place to get to know anyone than in a car as you have no escape. I spent the journeys telling her how famous I was going to be when I played at Wimbledon. Since being diagnosed with RA Mum has constantly supported me, just as she did when I played tennis. My loss has been hers too because she shared my hopes and dreams.

'I did finally tell my mother about Gerald six weeks after we met.'

'Why then?'

'Well, that was after Gerald took me up to the attic, I needed to tell her what had happened. It was quite a shock.'

'What happened?'

'We were at Mary's dance, and Gerald was behaving in a most strange way.'

March 1921

Gerald led Margaret right up to the attic stairs in the servants' quarters, and they sat down on the steps, alone in the darkness. The only thing they could hear was the faint sound of the band. Margaret adjusted the clips in her dark hair. Gerald edged nearer, clearing his throat as if leading up to something important. Just ask her you fool, he said to himself as he leaned forward, his face almost touching hers. He had to ask her. He knew his life had irreversibly changed six weeks ago, the moment he had met her.

'I'm sorry Gerald, can't this wait?' Margaret asked before he had the chance to begin. 'I've been booked to dance. It's Mary's party and we can't stay up here.'

'No, it can't wait!' Gerald insisted, raising his voice unintentionally.

Margaret was taken aback. 'Oh, I'm sure it can. The music for the next dance has begun.' She felt too shy to be with Gerald on her own. She walked back downstairs and into the arms of her next dancing partner.

Gerald stood up. 'Damn,' he said. 'Damn and blast.'

A few dances later Gerald claimed Margaret as his partner and led her up to the attic stairs again. Before she had hardly sat down, he asked, 'Will you marry me?'

'But I hardly know you,' Margaret stammered. 'I'm only seventeen. I can't marry you. Can't we wait?' She looked at Gerald. 'Please don't be upset,' she pleaded.

'How long do I have to wait?'

'Eighteen months. If we still feel the same then I will marry you.'

Gerald held his head in his hands. Eighteen months, he thought with despair. He was shocked. He was distraught to be rejected when he had been certain that she would say yes. He knew she was young and that they had not known each other long. Yet he could not imagine being married to anyone else. She was the only one for him. He took her hand. 'I'll wait,' he promised.

'My mother told me that it was a great honour to be proposed to, and that I should feel extremely flattered,' Granny tells me.

'I can't believe you said no,' I sigh to Granny. 'Why did you say no?'

'I was too young!' she cries with exasperation. 'I would have been a hopeless wife. I was having too much fun, I didn't want to be tied down.'

Put like that it makes me realise she was right. 'What did you do in those eighteen months?'

'The summer parties continued. I visited my brothers Willie and Ned at Cambridge and mixed with Ned's naval friends. Like Gerald, they had fought young in the war. The balls were held in marquees on the college grounds. We danced all night and ate eggs and bacon in the market place at five in the morning. It was great fun. During the autumn and winter months I went to Scotland and went to the Northern Meeting at Inverness. We went to...'

'Hang on, what's this Meeting thing?'

'What was I eating?' she says, sticking out her chin.

'No, what's the Northern Meeting?'

'A series of balls. The men wore colourful kilts representing the different clans or tail coats.'

'What did the women wear?'

'We wore silk evening dresses. The men also wore colourful stockings. We danced the "Eightsome Reels", the "Gay Gordons" and "Strip the Willow", where you lined up and faced your partner.' She starts humming the tune flatly. 'We danced all night and went home in daylight. I tried to sleep during the day as the dances were two nights running. They were wonderful,' she sighs nostalgically. 'In the winter we went to shooting parties. Gerald was one of the finest shots, something he'd inherited from his father who had a lovely shooting estate in Norfolk. I remember your grandfather carrying a gun which shot five cartridges without reloading. He shot four pheasants and one partridge.'

'The birds didn't stand a chance,' I say.

'Not a chance,' Granny repeats with a dry laugh. 'I went to hunt balls too. For the balls you were often given programmes. Alongside each dance you had to pencil in the name of your partner.'

It reminds me of a Jane Austen film. 'Did you see Gerald at these parties?'

'Oh yes, many times. His Aunt Mildred wanted us to get

together. I think she liked me.'

'How do you know?' I ask, thinking she sounds a bit too pleased with herself.

'Well, it was obvious. She used to invite me to stay for the weekends at her house, Stanmore, when Gerald was there. She was the one who told me Gerald was awarded an MC for his bravery in the war. Mildred was an avid Christian Scientist, she read endless books about it. She used to read them to me occasionally.'

'Did it interest you?'

'No, I thought it was frightfully dull.'

'I suppose it wouldn't have been the "done" thing to tell her to shut up. Christian Scientists believe illnesses can be cured with the power of prayer rather than medicine, don't they, Granny?'

'Yes, that's right.'

There's little chance of me becoming one then. 'Gerald wasn't at all religious, was he?'

'No! Not at all. He called men in Holy Orders, "God botherers"! He only went to church at Christmas but he still maintained very high moral principles and expected them of others too.'

'Did you meet anyone else apart from Gerald?'

'There were other men dead keen to marry me, some men old enough to be my father and I had to keep them all at arms length. Desmond was very persistent, he wouldn't let me alone. He was a crashing bore. One night I had to dance the whole night with another man called Kenneth to avoid him!'

'He sounds slimy.'

'Yes he was slimy!' Granny laughs. I smile, thinking that it is probably the first time she has ever said the word 'slimy' about a man.

'Weren't you worried Gerald might marry someone else?'

'No, not at all,' Granny says firmly.

'But he did meet someone else didn't he?'

'Yes, he did. A year or so after his proposal he started "stepping out" with a young girl but I don't think it was anything serious. You didn't really "go out" with people like you do today. He took her to the dances, that's all.'

'You weren't jealous?'

'No.'

'Come on, you must have been?'

'No,' she insists sharply as if to say, 'you've asked me that already.' Granny's arms and legs are defensively crossed, her mouth firmly shut. How am I going to get Granny to say anything a tiny bit more surprising or intimate? Perhaps I have to respect it's a generation thing. After all, saying nothing sometimes says more than anything else.

'Are you sure it didn't bother you? You weren't the tiniest bit worried that you'd missed your chance? I would have been.'

She bites her tongue. 'Well, he did cool off towards me. I remember at one party he danced with this girl all night, didn't ask me to dance once.'

'He probably did that on purpose.' I can't help thinking, Good for Gerald! Granny had asked him to wait. He didn't feel he was receiving great encouragement and his eighteen-month stint wasn't being shortened. He was trying to take control, play the game too. It's just the sort of thing we do today to make someone jealous.

'Yes, I should think he did,' Granny nods.

'Well, it's lucky it didn't worry you, that you weren't at all jealous.'

'I suppose I was jealous,' she admits quickly now. 'Very jealous. I didn't say anything to him though.'

Of course you didn't. That would be far too forward. 'What did you think?'

Granny looks as though she means business. 'I'm going to get my man back.'

'Had you kissed him yet?'

'No, we'd had a little cuddle, and a little grope. But that's all.'

A little grope? Did she mean to say that? It is impossible to imagine having the same kind of relationship today, where you hadn't held hands, nor even kissed in nearly two years. 'Why is it so hard to meet people today?' I ask her.

'I think that your generation tie yourselves down to one man whereas we went out with lots of different people. We were much freer. I met so many people in those eighteen months that it was easy for me to realise that I didn't want to be with anyone else but Gerald. I was certain that I was in love with him.' Her mouth droops as she adds finally, 'I can't bear the word, "partner".'

'No, I can't stand it either. How did you go about getting Gerald back?'

'I asked him down for a weekend at Folkestone. My father owned a property there. I think they both knew I was keen on Gerald.'

'That you loved him?'

'Yes, I loved him,' she says gently with a soft smile, 'and I knew he still loved me.'

CHAPTER FIVE

I tiptoe into the sitting room. Granny has an hour's nap after lunch. She always likes to eat a cheddar cheese and pickle sandwich, followed by a cup of coffee and two chunks of Bourneville chocolate. I look at my watch. She's only had forty minutes. Shall I wake her up? She looks fast asleep, the blue checked rug pulled closely around her, mouth open with dark chocolate coated in the corners and her favourite Mozart CD blasting out in the background. I decide to let her have the full hour as I want her to feel rested for the next session. I gently close the door behind me but then hear a loud snort, followed by, 'Is it time?'

I come back into the room. 'Yes,' I say. 'An hour goes quickly doesn't it. Would you like an arm?'

Granny is at the edge of her chair, preparing herself to move. She has been in this poised position for five minutes now. It's a look I recognise too well. When my RA was at its most intense I needed lifting. Mum and I would count, 'One, two, three,' followed by a 'Well done,' when all I had done was finally stand on my feet. Occasionally it would be much easier and quicker if Granny allowed us to help. But it is this dogged determination that keeps her independent.

'Well done,' I find myself praising, when she finally reaches the sofa-bed. We start work again. Today I want to talk to her about the engagement. I am curious about the in-laws. 'Was Gerald well-off?' I begin.

'No, not at all. We only had £1,500 a year to live on which

wasn't a great deal.'

'That didn't worry you?'

'That didn't what?' she says sleepily. I don't think she has totally woken up. I ask her the question again.

'No. When my mother asked if Gerald had any private means I said, "He must be well-off, he even has a car, Mother, a Buick!"'

I find this endearing and naïve. She was only nineteen. 'How did he propose?'

'We were in Folkestone when he proposed.'

'Did you know he was going to ask you?'

'Yes, I sensed it,' she nods gently, her eyes closed. 'I had asked him there, hoping that he would propose.'

'What did he say?'

November 1922

'Margaret,' Gerald turned to her in the dining room and put an arm around her waist. The room was dark and musty. He wanted to ask her before they joined her parents in the sitting room. He was certain that she would say yes this time. 'I think we should get married,' he said calmly. He hadn't rehearsed what he was going to say, he didn't feel nervous this time. He sensed that Margaret had asked him to Folkestone for a reason.

Margaret immediately rested a hand on top of his. 'Yes, I think we should.' Gerald broke into a smile as he took her hand into his. They sat down for a moment in the dark. Gerald leaned forward and kissed her on the lips. Margaret's heart jumped wildly at the closeness of his touch. Was she dreaming? She had never kissed anyone before, well not like this, and she was excited by the passionate feelings it evoked in her. She wanted him to kiss her again. He wished that they could be on their own to discuss the future but, 'We must ask your mother and father,' he said.

'Yes, we must. They will be thrilled,' Margaret replied. Please kiss me again, she was thinking.

They walked into the drawing room, looking like cats who had just stolen the cream and eaten it as well. Gerald cleared his throat and stepped forward awkwardly, asking Margaret's father if he could speak to him in private.

Margaret watched them intently as they walked out of the room. She wanted to shout out that she was engaged. She paced up and down the sitting room, sat down, stood up again, sat down and then sprang out of her chair one final time like a cuckoo in a clock.

'Please, Margaret, either sit down or stand up,' Mother said to her curiously. 'Come Margaret, tell me about it.'

'Oh Mother,' she burst out. 'The most exciting thing has happened. Gerald has proposed!'

Mother put down her sewing. 'Oh my darling, what wonderful news.'

'Yes, isn't it,' Margaret sighed happily. She could hear voices in the next door room.

'My parents have an estate in Norfolk, Witchingham,' Gerald was explaining.

Father asked him more about his family and his income. 'Do you have any private means?'

'I have my army pay but little more besides.' Gerald could sense he needed to say more. 'I intend to look after her as best as I can.'

Father looked at Gerald. The man standing before him was

not a Duke or a Marquess with rich estates, but he was an honourable man. He liked him. Above all he wanted his Marka to be happy.

He finally shook Gerald's hand, 'Congratulations. You take care of her. She's so very young.'

Gerald nodded. 'I promise.'

They returned to the sitting room, Gerald smiling as he overheard, 'He must be well off, Mother, he even has a car, a Buick!'

'I'm afraid my older sisters were a bit jealous when I became engaged. My oldest sister, Jeane was already married, but Kitty and Betty, who were both older than me and single were jealous because they didn't get out as much. But my brothers were thrilled,' Granny concludes.

'Were Gerald's family rich?'

'No, they weren't very rich. They didn't install electricity until after we were married in 1923. They continued using carrying candles and paraffin lamps. We had electricity at Longford in 1912 or 13. It was a joy! Did I tell you Gerald's grandfather made a lot of money in a copper mine in Portugal?'

'No, you didn't. Where did Gerald's parents live?'

'Great Witchingham Hall in Norfolk.'

'Is Great Witchingham Hall the house where Bernard Matthews lives now?'

'That's right, with the turkeys.'

I recalled a time when Dad was chairing one of his general knowledge sessions, over Sunday lunch.

'Helen, what was the date of the Battle of the Somme?'

Dad asked at the kitchen table.

'1916, I think,' she answered tentatively, looking at Dad.

'Correct,' he said as he added another point on to Helen's score. 'Alice, your question now. What is the capital of Turkey?'

'That's easy,' I replied. 'Bernard Matthews.'

'What did Gerald's father do?' I ask, still smiling at this memory.

'He owned quite a large estate, about two thousand acres. The land was let out to farmers but he kept the shooting rights. He was the most wonderful fisherman.'

'When did you first meet them?'

'After our weekend at Folkestone, we motored down on the Monday.'

'Were you nervous?'

'Well I was rather.' Granny shifts her bottom on the sofa-bed. 'I never told you the men wore gloves when they were dancing, short white ones.'

'OK, but back to the in-laws. Tell me about them.' I want to hear a good story.

'I've still got my gloves, they're rather hard now though.'

'Granny! Back to the in-laws, tell me about them,' I say, trying to steer her away from the dances. 'What did Gerald's father look like?'

'William, was fair to grey and quite tall with a moustache.'

'Was he similar in character to Gerald?'

'In some ways. William was a terrific sportsman. He invented dry fly fishing for salmon, you know, and was one of the best shots in England. Gerald took after him there. He was also very even-tempered like his son. I can't help thinking he was rather a selfish man though. His whole life followed the Game seasons. He salmon fished from February to August, shot grouse from August onwards, and then went on to partridges and then pheasants until the following February. And on it went again.'

'How boring.'

'His wife, Lady Grace, loved hunting but was never allowed a horse. She didn't enjoy the shooting but she did wake up for the parties because she loved the company. She was a gifted story-teller just like Gerald.'

'Can you remember any of the stories?'

'No, not really.'

'What was Gerald's mother like?'

'Grace was tiny with light-brown hair which she coiled into a bun. I think she can have been no more than five foot, weighing about six stone. She had hazel eyes and a large nose. I thought she looked like a frog, but she did have the most beautiful hands. She wore rings on practically every finger.'

'What did she do?' I smile, thinking about the 'frog' description.

'Well, she was very clever but she didn't do any public works. She wasn't really a country woman so I think she became excruciatingly bored of married life. That's probably why she was a terrible hypochondriac. She spent most of her time in bed,' Granny relays. 'She was constantly ill with either a throat infection or cough.' Granny smiles as if she is remembering a story. 'A friend called round to Witchingham, hoping to see her,' she starts again. 'The butler answered the door, and said, "You cannot see her ladyship, she has gone to bed for two years!"'

'Is that really true?' I ask sceptically.

'Yes!' she laughs. 'In fact she was quite ill when Gerald and I were in Africa. Her doctor discovered a swelling on her heart as big as a golf ball. Apparently she was a freak case and should have died years ago. She lived to a grand age though.' Granny's voice croaks so she stops to have a drink of lemon squash. She puts down the glass and continues, 'She was eccentric but in a funny way I was fond of her. She used to wear the most awful baggy brown skirts that swamped her. She spent I don't know what-and-all on clothes and had a fetish for shoes. When she died they found about fifty pairs, all handmade in Paris, but no one could wear them because her feet were so small, like Cinderella's!' she shrieks as she rocks herself forward keeping her arms crossed. 'She always sat with her feet on the sofa, even when visitors were around, and she felt the cold dreadfully.' Granny leans back against the cushion. 'She shivered around the house, leaving a trail of hot-water bottles which fell out of her baggy jerseys.'

'I think she sounds great.' Anyone who likes hot-water bottles is on my wavelength.

'Well, she was unusual and rather scatty. She wasn't very punctual for dinner. My father got very irritated with her when she didn't come down on the stroke of 8.30pm. Did I ever tell you that she travelled to Kenya in 1910 on safari and brought home two lion cubs? One died, but the other lived and became her pet.'

'No way?'

'Yes! She adored it! She looked after it as if it were her dog. She called it Rumaruti.'

'Where did she keep it? In a doggy basket?'

'Under her bed. When she was not well she told the nurse to be careful, "There's a lion under my bed." The nurse just thought she was gaga, telling her to hush, until she saw an enormous great paw stretch out and touch her leg.'

Unusual? I think she was mad. 'Tell me more,' I insist.

'The neighbours insisted she get rid of it at once. You see,' Granny explains in a more serious tone, 'they too had owned a lion which they kept in a cage, but it killed their teenage son. The young boy had opened the cage to feed it and the lion went for him. Grace sent Rumaruti to Bristol Zoo but he wouldn't eat, he just pined for her. When she visited him he started to eat again but it was hopeless, she knew she could not stay so she had him put down.'

'That's a really sad story Granny.'

'Yes, it was rather. She had an interesting upbringing,' she carries on, 'Grace's father was the Earl of Dunmore and he built an enormous house on Harris, up in the Hebrides, because he thought Queen Victoria was going to come and stay with him. He spent all his money on this house. It was called Armandsuy, I think it's still there. He had to sell all his property between Glasgow and Perth and they lived a life of wandering around without any home. Grace spent most of her childhood abroad.'

'Going back to this house they built in Harris, did Queen Victoria go and stay with them?'

'No, never.'

'So it was a waste of time.'

'Yes, a waste of time. He spent all his money on the house and the Queen never came.'

'What an extraordinary thing to do,' I say as I scribble

down the story, at the same time watching Granny's reactions closely.

'Yes, an extraordinary thing to do!' Granny repeats emphatically. 'It's hardly surprising Grace was so eccentric really. I will always remember her at William's funeral. She was sitting on the window seat in the dining room, a tiny little figure looking out into the distance. Tears were rolling down her cheeks.'

'That is sad,' I reflect. It seems like no one paid her any attention so she withdrew into her own world, Granny?'

'I think that's right. Grace's sister, Evelyn, was as mad as a hatter. She became a Muslim and, dressing up as a man, took part in a pilgrimage to Mecca. You see, only men were allowed to do that. Later on she became involved in some court case to do with a woman and her Pekinese and she held up the proceedings for several days because she refused to swear on the Bible. A Koran had to be obtained.' Before I have a chance to gasp at this story, Granny carries on, 'I must tell you, Gerald's parents had a dreadful cook called Julia.'

I smile at the way Granny's mouth drooped when she said, 'Julia'. 'What were Gerald's sisters like, Esther and Nancy?'

'I met them when I arrived at Witchingham, they had stayed up with their governess to see me. They were both very fair. Nancy was beautiful, but they wore dud clothes. Esther loved to bet on the horses.'

'Was she a good gambler?'

'No, she never won a thing.'

It sounds just like my brother Tom who has an obsession with fruit machines. He never wins either. I tell him he might as well chuck his money down a drain. 'Can you describe

Witchingham, Granny?'

'It was very dark with lots of little rooms, it reminded me of a rabbit warren. Quite creepy but I grew to like it. I remember the dark panelled doors and being shown to my bedroom with a carrying candle by my bedside.'

'Would Gerald have been allowed in your bedroom?'

'NO, no. But he did creep in the morning after we had arrived. I saw his blond hair poking round the door. "Good morning darling," he whispered. "Gerald!" I said. "What are you doing?!" He walked into the room in his blue dressing-gown and navy striped pyjamas and kissed me on the cheek.' As Granny says this I can tell she is visualising the scene in her head. There are no signs of sleep in her eyes now. 'I noticed he had shaved already,' she goes on, as if she can feel his smooth skin. 'I think he wanted to see what I looked like first thing in the morning.'

'How naughty of him,' I say, thinking how innocent it was. 'I'm sure he looked gorgeous in a dressing gown, Granny.'

'Yes, I'm sure he did. I was too worried we'd be caught out so I hardly dared look at him. I remember breakfast was a stilted affair. Gerald told me afterwards that Grace had seen him outside my room and thought it very infra-dig[1]. "Wait until you're married for that kind of thing," she had said sternly. "Infra-dig!" she repeated. We both had a giggle about it.'

'Did Gerald kiss you a lot after you were engaged?'

'Did Gerald cook for me?'

'No, kiss you?'

'No, not much, not until we were married.'

'Tell me about your wedding.'

'We were married on 28 February 1923 at St Peter's

---

[1] Undignified

Church, Eaton Square, London.' Granny is clever the way she remembers dates and times. She even remembers one of the hymns, Lead us heavenly father lead us, but I need more than that. Facts, dates, times – they aren't interesting. I want to hear about the day itself, the emotion, what she wore. 'Tell me more,' I push. 'I need to be able to imagine it, Granny.'

28 February 1923

Margaret was shaking on the arm of her father. The port he had given her the night before to calm nerves and help her sleep hadn't worked.

Her father felt immensely proud to be giving her away. Jeane had got married first, but he had not been able to lead her up the aisle as her wedding was during the war, when he was in India.

Aunts nudged and sighed in their decorative hats, friends and family gazed at Margaret from every angle. Five brides-maids followed behind her – among them were Gerald's two sisters, Esther and Nancy, and Margaret's younger sister, Helen, dressed in a cloud of pink dresses and lace caps.

The church was packed with at least two hundred people. Granny Balfour was sitting with Margaret's mother. Granny Radnor, who was wheeled in her chair, resolute not to miss the event, sat at the side of the front pew. Margaret's brothers and sisters were behind her parents, along with Mary Thynne and her friends. A bus load of employees from Longford had been brought up to London. Nanny Cutt watched her walking down the aisle. She felt as if she were watching her own daughter get married. 'Doesn't Margaret look beautiful?' her neighbour whispered to her.

'Ssh,' Nanny Cutt replied firmly, her eyes still on the bride.

Gerald's friends were sparse in comparison. He had lost many men friends during the war. However, he still had some close friends from the Coldstream. Lady Grace, sitting next to Gerald's father, William, was wearing a blue dress and hat, with matching pointed shoes and blue rings on her fingers. As she watched Margaret, she decided that she would take her future titled daughter-in-law to many dinner parties after she was married, she could show her off on her arm to all the aunts. Lady Mildred Fitzgerald and her husband sat behind them. What luck it was that she had sat them next to each other at her luncheon party.

Margaret took another step. The family veil was heavy and the wreath of myrtle and flowers in her hair did not feel secure. She was hardly aware of who was in the church. Please don't let anything go wrong, she prayed as she felt her long ivory satin dress with its bow at the back and small train travel one more step towards Gerald and Hubert, Gerald's brother and best man.

Gerald looked at her reassuringly. She smiled back before they both turned to face the parson.

'Will you take this...'

'I will!' Gerald declared loudly before the parson had even finished the question.

Margaret started to giggle as she watched the parson repeat the vows. He looked a little put out. 'Will you take this woman to be your wife? To have and to hold from this day forward, for better for worse, for richer for poorer...'

'I will,' Gerald finally replied at the right time.

There was a Guard of Honour outside the church, eight

Coldstream Guards non-commissioned officers stood with their swords upheld to make an archway. Gerald and Margaret walked through, arm in arm. One photograph was taken outside the church before the wedding guests made their way to No 81, Eaton Square, for the reception.

Wedding presents were laid out in the drawing-room; silver candlesticks stood on display, along with a chiming clock, silver sugar basins, a dessert service, silver canteen, jewellery and a Moroccan leather dressing case from her mother, beautifully fitted with silver-backed brushes and combs and crystal bottles with silver caps. A detective had been hovering in the drawing-room during the church service, guarding these valuable pieces.

Names were called out, Margaret and Gerald shaking the hands of each guest.

Towards the end of the party, she and Gerald cut the cake with Gerald's sword. As the sword touched the base she closed her eyes and held very still.

'To Gerald and Margaret,' her father raised his champagne glass. 'We drink to your health.'

'Your very good health!' everyone cheered.

Margaret and Gerald went upstairs to change into their going-away outfits. Margaret slipped on a grey silk dress with a grey feathered hat. As she descended the stairs, she threw the bouquet of flowers. There was a cry of delight and great cheers as Helen hugged them to her chest.

Margaret kissed her parents and Gerald's parents goodbye. Her mother was tearful.

'Did you make a wish?' Gerald asked her as they motored away to start their honeymoon.

Margaret had made three wishes in one. 'I wish for lots of children,' she had said, 'and to be happy, whatever the future holds.' And then there had been just one more thing, she thought smiling, 'Please may my honeymoon night be wonderful and may I satisfy Gerald. There, that's it, no more wishes I promise.' She turned to Gerald and smiled. 'Yes, I did, but I'm not going to tell you what. It's bad luck.'

CHAPTER SIX

Granny is sitting on the sofa-bed already, keen for the next session. She is staying with us for longer than intended so we can continue with our research. Each morning before I manage even to say the routine, 'Hello, did you sleep well?' she says, 'Alice, I forgot to mention to you that...' And she tells me another story. I am delighted both that it is such fun for her to look back into the past and that she is able to remember so much. She is astonishing.

However, I know the time has come to ask her about her honeymoon night and I'm not looking forward to this session.

'Can you ask Granny about sex?' I ask Mum quietly in the kitchen whilst she is ironing some silk.

'I couldn't, it would be too embarrassing,' Mum replies. 'It will be much better coming from you.' She laughs at me as I take a deep breath.

'Oh go on, please?' I try again.

'Alice! It's your book, you must do it, now shoo!'

I pull a face at her and go to join Granny.

'Hi Granny,' I say with an unnatural brightness. I sit down to my computer and decide to check my e-mails first.

She sits up eagerly. 'Have you got the tape ready?'

'Just checking my e-mails first.'

'Checking what?' she warbles.

'E-mails,' I repeat. 'It's like receiving mail over the computer.'

'Oh I see,' she nods knowingly although clearly she does not have a clue. What I have just said to her is as alien as saying I come from the planet Mars.

'I've got a message from a friend in Australia.'

'A message from Australia, darling?'

'Yes, amazing isn't it? None of this waiting for three weeks to receive a letter like in your day. We can receive messages in seconds.'

'Amazing, I can't think how it works. I want to tell you about our honeymoon now,' she begins, not at all impressed by the subject of e-mails.

Great, maybe it won't be so difficult after all. 'OK,' I say, pressing Record.

'Is the tape on?'

'Yes, ready now. Go for it.'

'We had the most wonderful honeymoon, Gerald took me to Biarritz and it was the first time I had travelled on a night train. We also stayed in an inn and went fishing.'

No! I have to ask her about the honeymoon night, to get the nitty gritty. 'Granny, can we pause for a moment,' I cough. 'Can we go back to your honeymoon night?'

'Well, my honeymoon night was at Stanmore. We had a lovely time playing golf.'

More trivial facts. But how can I expect her to reveal any intimate secrets? Why should she? If I really want to know I'm just going to have to come out with it. 'Were you nervous about sleeping with Gerald for the first time?' There, done it.

'Was I what?' She leans forward and sticks out her chin.

'Nervous about sleeping with Gerald, having sex Granny.'

Granny crosses her arms tightly and slides her false teeth around. 'No, not at all,' she replies sharply.

I could simply move on, but... 'You weren't a bit nervous?' I persevere. I need to ask her this because I believe her answers will say so much about how times have changed.

'I knew absolutely nothing about it. Nothing! I didn't understand what it meant.'

'Did you not read about it or talk to friends?'

'I talked to my mother and Mary but up until then I hadn't a clue. I remember Mother saying I had great "sex appeal" but I didn't know what it meant. I didn't even realise how babies were made,' she says shaking her head incredulously. 'I remember Mother looking embarrassed and awkward when she talked to me.'

February 1923

Margaret was lying in bed, dreaming about married life. Her mother opened the door and perched at the end of her bed. She didn't sit down comfortably, in fact she looked as though she were about to fall on to the floor. She cleared her throat as if she were leading up to something important.

'Mother, is anything wrong?' Margaret asked, sitting up.

'Margaret darling, do you know what is involved in marriage?' she said finally, keeping her head down.

Margaret looked at her blankly.

'Have you and Gerald spoken about starting a family?' she asked. 'Do you know what is involved?'

'No, we haven't spoken about it yet, Mother.'

'Well,' she said, shifting slightly, 'the most important rule is that if a husband wants sex, you should fall in with his wishes.'

Margaret stared at her. Eventually she muttered, 'I will, Mother.'

'Good.' She stood up. 'Your honeymoon is near so it is

Margaret, 1904

View of Longford Castle from the River Avon

Jacob, 6th Earl of Radnor, 1914

Julian, the Countess of Radnor, 1914

Brothers and sisters, New Year, 1924: back row standing, from left to right, Willie, Helen, Anty, Barty and Ned; middle standing, from left to right, Kitty and Betty; at front, sitting, from left to right, Jeane, Margaret and Peter.

Margaret and Ned

Margaret with friends at the
Cottenham Race Meeting

Margaret and Peter with the Hunt at Longford

Gerald as a captain in the Coldstream Guards, 1921

Margaret's engagement photograph, 1922

Gerald (left) with his father,
shooting at Witchingham

Margaret with Anne

Gerald with Anne, 1924

important to know these things.' She left the room.

The colour in Margaret's face vanished. Why hadn't anyone talked to her about this 'sex' thing before? Did Mary know anything about it? If she did why hadn't she told her? Well, how did you do it? How often would Gerald want sex? Once a month? Once a year? How long did it take? All these thoughts began to worry her.

Margaret felt too self-conscious and shy to ask her mother any more about it. Besides, it had vexed her mother to tell her as much as she had. Whatever sex meant, it must have been important for her to broach the subject in the first place.

She asked Mary instead.

'Margaret, you are naïve!' she said with a glint in her eye, 'I know all about it!'

'Thank heavens,' Margaret smiled. 'But how on earth do you know?' she sighed, feeling ashamed to know so little about life.

'Oh, I've read heaps about "the facts of life". These are the golden rules about sex,' she said authoritatively. 'Number one, always keep your mouth shut, as closed as you'd like to see a crocodile's mouth.'

Margaret threw her a startled look.

'Number two, certainly turn off the lights. It would be too embarrassing to see the man. Besides, groping and pinching in the dark is far more exciting,' she giggled. 'Number three, try not to smile. Submissive is the name of the game,' she carried on, her expression as happy as a child just given a chocolate treat. She was delighted to be of such help.

Mary flashed Margaret a big sister, worldly smile. 'Oh,' she panicked, horrified to have forgotten the last vital instruction. 'Buy a towel, or plenty of face cloths and lay them out on the bed.' She scrunched her brown eyes as she said, 'That is a must, you see, it's all rather a messy business.'

I cannot get over how innocent Granny was. I was expecting her to be inexperienced, and certainly a virgin before she was married – but not even to know how babies were made? 'Did you and Gerald talk about starting a family?'

'No, never, it just happened.' No going to the family planning clinics then. 'I never refused Gerald and I did enjoy it.'

That's lucky, I want to say. 'I'm sure Gerald was affectionate.'

'He was, but all our sexual activity was confined to the bedroom. We didn't kiss much during the day but we did hold hands,' she continues.

'Can you remember your honeymoon night?'

'Yes, vividly. We were at Mildred's home in Stanmore. As part of her present, she gave us her house to enjoy for three nights before we travelled to Biarritz. I must tell you my father bought me a lovely trousseau. Pink crepe-de-chine petticoats, a Harvey Nichols fur coat, lace nightgowns...'

I cut in, trying to bring her back to the night itself. 'Tell me more about the night.'

'Mother bought me some lovely pink knickers, sorry what did you say?' At that moment the phone rings, the clocks around the house start chiming, and Jasmine, my miniature dachshund, flies into the room like a dog on speed and starts furiously biting the curtain. Meggy, the older Norwich Terrier with a cauliflower ear, slowly joins us, rubbing her bottom along the floor. 'Jasmine, piss off, uh go away! Meggy, stop doing that!' I don't feel comfortable swearing in front of

Granny. In all her ninety-six years I have never heard her swear, not even say 'damn'.

'Al-ice,' Mum shrills, coming into our room, 'it's the dentist's secretary for you. Apparently you've missed your last three appointments and have a £15 fine. Oh Meggy, have you got worms again?' she says, scooping her up and then holding her nose. 'Oh, who's got fish breath.' In despair I pick up the phone.

Ten minutes later I turn back to Granny and take a deep breath, 'I'm still banging on about your honeymoon night.' This is the one time I'm glad Granny is blind as she can't see me go red asking these questions. 'Can you tell me more about the night itself?'

'No, not really,' she replies defensively, her arms held close around her so as not to allow anyone into the secret of her honeymoon night.

I realise there's no point pushing her on something so personal although I wish she would open up. She's doing well but I need more intimate stories. Granny must sense my disappointment because as I am about to tell her our session is over she suddenly says, 'I remember the morning after our honeymoon night.'

February 1923

'Darling, can you bring me my slippers?' Gerald shouted from the bathroom. Margaret found them at the side of the bed, and walked down the cold passage. She stood tentatively out-side the door, she did not dare walk in. Instead she threw them in. They flew across the floor like aeroplanes. One hit the side of the bath.

'Oh Margaret! Bring me my slippers properly!' Gerald laughed.

Margaret walked into the bathroom with her head bowed, and picked them up. She had never thought about seeing Gerald with no clothes on. Mary had always said to turn the lights off but she could hardly do that in broad daylight! What was she going to do? She did not know how to behave, where to look. He climbed out of the bath and touched her cheek. He kissed her on the forehead and cupped a hand under her chin. Margaret finally looked at him and smiled. 'We're married now my darling girl,' he said. 'Please don't be shy. We're married now.'

CHAPTER SEVEN

'When did you start thinking about going to Africa?'

'A good year later. It was after Anne was born. She was an adorable baby with very dark hair.'

'Did Gerald say why he wanted to go?' I ask, trying to keep on the same subject.

'He was bored of peace-time soldiering and it was difficult to get jobs.'

'Gerald might have wanted to start a new life to leave behind the memories of the war?' I suggest.

Granny rejects the idea immediately.

'No, no, we just wanted a new adventure, that's all.'

I know it was not as clear-cut as that because Uncle Richard told me that Gerald went to Africa because he needed to put the past behind him. His friends had died. There was no opening for him at Witchingham. Nothing was left for him. It does not surprise me that Gerald did not share these deep feelings with Margaret. He would have wanted her to see it as an adventure, not as an escape.

I try her once more with the same question of why exactly they decided to go.

'I've told you,' she replies brusquely.

'Well, you haven't really Granny. There must be more to it. Don't you think the horrors of the war must have had a really profound effect on him?'

'Yes, I should think they did,' she sniffs as she wrinkles her nose.

'What other reasons can you think of?'

Granny leans back. 'He was probably a bit tired of doing the "social rounds". He wasn't a great party person like me.'

My silence is telling her I want to hear more.

'Also, his work did worry him. It didn't pay well.'

April 1923

Margaret was anxious about Gerald. Something had changed since returning home after their honeymoon. Hubert, his brother, had just been axed from the Navy and Gerald was upset for him. They were reducing numbers after the war and Hubert was one of the unlucky ones. 'He's emigrating to Kenya to go into partnership and become a coffee planter,' he told Margaret over dinner.

'Really? What an odd thing to do,' Margaret replied.

Gerald disagreed and then told her he was bored stiff by peace-time soldiering, with all its ceremonial duties. He had just been on duty with his company for the wedding of Lady Elizabeth Bowes-Lyon and the Duke of York. 'I need to have a change too,' he thought as he put his plate aside.

Yet he did not know what he wanted to do. Hubert's dismissal was yet another sign that the forces didn't really need them any more. Besides, if he stayed he couldn't climb the ladder quickly because the army system of promotion was based on age. He was faced with the endless plodding from being Captain to Major to Lieutenant-Colonel and so on. He felt he had reached a dead end.

Margaret, on the other hand, wished she was back on honeymoon. She let her mind visit again their most exciting night at the casino in San Sebastian. Gerald played roulette. He won a fair amount but lost it all again. They had never laughed so much as they did that night walking back to their hotel, Gerald's pockets emptied of coins. Then they had travelled back to eastern France, Gerald wanting to re-visit old war haunts. I'm sure it helped him lay some ghosts to rest, Margaret thought uneasily. That was where the trouble had started. She was sure things would soon fit into place. Gerald would settle down. She told herself not to worry any more.

Gerald lay awake at night thinking about the future. He did not want to stay in England. He was haunted by the image of the burnt out fields in Eastern France. He had looked back, many times, to the day he revisited them. Groups of farmers had been busy working on the battlefields, trying to re-cultivate the land and fill the shell holes. He watched Margaret as she stared across the field to the gaunt skeleton trees with their dead, black, burnt out branches. He had been hesitant whether to bring her here but Margaret was strong and didn't seem upset. She was sheltered from the grim realities of war.

'When were you wounded?' she asked as they stood arm in arm looking at the workers in the field. Margaret brushed a strand of hair from her eyes.

'Twice, in 1915 and 1917. That's what saved me.' Gerald shook his head and released his arm from Margaret's. 'To think I believed that the war would be over by Christmas. That's what all my friends thought.'

'I remember my grandmother in her dressing gown with a black sealskin coat over the top trying to play draughts or read me stories over the sound of the Zeppelin raids. It seemed exciting. I was even envious of my brother Barty for seeing the Potters Bar Zeppelin burst into flames,' she reflected incredulously. 'I saw terrible injuries at Longford when Mother turned it into a hospital. We all lived in fear that we might receive a telegram saying my brother Ned or my father were gone. But I did not lose anyone I loved.' She turned to Gerald waiting for him to say something but he didn't say a word. He didn't even seem to be listening.

He was thinking about all the friends he had lost.

Gerald could still hear the deafening crashes and see the distorted bodies lying outside the dug-outs. It was the most vile sight on earth which he could not describe to anyone. It would always be with him, but he had to try and lock it away in a dark corner within himself and never turn the key. He would never forget the smell of the blood, the mud, the stench, the rats, the FEAR that you were the next one to die. That fear ate away inside him, it would scar him for life. He knew that the only way to make the scar fade was to leave the army. He had to get away from Europe to start a new life, leaving behind the memories of all those lives lost.

Gerald turned over on to his other side. There was another reason too. With practically no private means and living on a captain's wage, it was beyond his pocket to keep Margaret in the style that was expected of him. He had to cover the expenses of a nanny, a cook, parlour maid, housemaid and a manservant. I can't afford it, he reasoned to himself. Nor do I want to.

He was not sure how to tell Margaret he wanted to go abroad. It would be easy for him to leave the country as he wasn't close to his family, especially now that his uncle, Mildred Fitzgerald's husband, was dead. He had been the colonel of Gerald's regiment, the Coldstream Guards, someone in whom Gerald had always confided. He was one of the last real friends Gerald had left in the army and his death in 1918 had hit hardest of all. To lose him when the war was almost over was unbearable. So, with that and Hubert on his way to Kenya, there was nothing to keep him in England. For Margaret, of course, things would be very different. She adored her large and happy family. She loved the parties, the dancing, the opera and the finery that had begun to bore him deeply. In fact she had already made him wait eighteen months so she could be free to enjoy herself. She had had so little time in society. But he found the endless social round a bore, plus the fact that they could not really afford to reciprocate. He knew he had to confide his worries. But was it fair to ask her to give it all up for him? Could she bear to leave her family and Longford behind?

These thoughts troubled his mind together with the need to find an exciting plan to present to Margaret. Where would they go? What would he do to support her? Surely there were more opportunities for them abroad? Nothing was left for him in England. He must get away.

November 1924

Gerald sent in his papers that summer, after completing his ten year stretch in the army. The idea of leaving England still occupied his thoughts constantly but he had felt unable to bring it up so soon after the birth of their first daughter, Anne. Now that Anne was seven months old, he felt he must speak to Margaret.

It was a Sunday morning. They were in bed, eating thin slices of bread and butter with tea. Gerald was summoning the courage to speak to Margaret. 'Margaret,' he said, his voice louder than usual, 'why don't we spend my "golden handshake" on a trip?' The army had given him a thousand pounds.

Margaret turned to him with a smile. 'A holiday?'

'Well, yes, but with a view to possibly settling abroad. Making a living abroad.' He had said it at last.

Her smile quickly faded. 'Where would we go?'

He took her hand. 'We need to think about that.' Gerald had been thinking about where to go for months. Initially he had liked the idea of Australia or Canada but then changed his mind. He liked the idea of Africa because Hubert was there. 'Think how exciting it would be to emigrate like Hubert.'

'I'm not sure I could leave England and my family. What about Anne?'

'Couldn't we give it a try? I don't feel that there are any opportunities for me here.'

Margaret did not know what to say. The idea of emigrating filled her with fear. Where would they go? What would they do? Her family would never forgive her, would they? She turned to Gerald again, about to ask if he had really thought this through. Yet when she looked at his face, searching for a response, and the vulnerability in his eyes, she realised that this was what had been haunting him since the honeymoon. He was looking at her as if his life depended on what she said next. 'Where would we go?' she asked tentatively.

Gerald immediately drew breath. He told her he had been thinking about going to Australia or Canada.

'No,' Margaret put her foot down, 'Australia's too far away, I would miss my family too much. Canada would be too cold.'

Gerald left Africa to last, as if it were his trump card. He talked to her about Hubert and his coffee planting and other ventures that they could explore. He looked at Margaret again, pleading for her to see the adventure and challenge that could lie ahead if she said yes. He felt as if he was asking her to marry him again. He feared her rejecting his idea just as she had rejected him the first time he had proposed. He knew how much he was asking of her. Yet, if she said 'no' he would be stuck in England, trapped in a life he did not want to lead.

Margaret was thinking hard. She felt such a deep pull towards Gerald. She could not bear to disappoint him. She loved him too much. This last year he has been unhappy and I understand he wants a change. It has also been hard to make ends meet. Perhaps there are opportunities in farming as Gerald says. We are young and have health on our side. We should take risks while we can.

'I will go on this trip,' Margaret said finally.

'You will?' Gerald repeated, unable to hide the flood of relief and excitement in his voice.

'I WILL,' she turned to him. Going to Africa would be an adventure. Above all she wanted to support Gerald in whatever he chose to do.

'So money was a big part of the reason, Granny.'

'Yes, it was. We were pushed. I think Gerald wanted the freedom and adventure too.'

'How did your parents react to you wanting to go to Africa?'

'A little bit shocked,' Granny takes time to think about what she is going to say next, 'but very encouraging,' she concludes. Again, a 'tie it up neatly' answer.

'They can't have wanted you to go,' I argue. 'I should think that even today mothers and fathers are not that keen about their children taking off abroad. If Helen said she was about to go to Outer Mongolia I don't think Mum and Dad would be jumping for joy. They would tell her not to go, saying it was a crazy idea. They were worried about her going to Africa for seven weeks. Anything can happen, you just don't know. It must have been even worse for your parents when communication was poor and Africa was so primitive.'

Granny is strangely silent. 'They were shocked, but they were encouraging,' she insists again.

I decide to change the subject. 'How lucky it was that you both wanted to go.'

'Yes, very lucky.'

'Did it scare you leaving home?'

'Well, I was excited. I had never been on a long sea voyage ever, only across the Channel to France. I wasn't scared, no, not at all.'

'But it's one thing going on holiday, another thing completely thinking you will settle out there for good.' I wait for her to say something. 'Granny?' I prompt her.

'Yes quite,' she says absent-mindedly. She looks lost in another world. I don't feel I am allowed to step into it with her right now. I am sure Granny did feel anxious about the future – who wouldn't in her position – but she would never have confessed to any fear.

I think it was a common trait of their generation to say what they thought they ought to say, rather than what they really wanted to say, or else to say nothing at all. I end our session thinking Granny looks tired. 'We're nearly ready to talk about Africa,' I tell her.

'Good,' she says as she stands up shakily. 'We were so happy at M'Coben.'

Once they had settled on the farm and overcome the initial challenges, Granny's homesickness comes across very powerfully through the letters. At times she was clearly miserable, bored and lonely with her 'deadly monotonous existence,' as she called it on occasion. I am looking forward to asking her about the loneliness and homesickness, but I am also dreading her lack of communication. She will see her homesickness as a weakness and refuse to admit to it.

My going to Africa is a challenge. But talking to Granny about her time there might be an even greater one.

CHAPTER EIGHT

'Sod it.'

'Oh Dad,' I frown, 'what have you done? You really must learn to use the computer.'

'Stop nagging. I'll learn in my own time.'

'Have you got a cash-point card yet?'

Dad smiles as he leaves the room. 'I like to go to my bank every day.'

Dad was just on-line, looking at car-hiring prices in Africa. Itineraries are being provisionally planned. He is trying to work out the best way to make the holiday work but we have not yet discussed it in detail.

After Dad leaves, I think about how much I want to go to Africa now. I have a chance to do something different. I have an opportunity to travel again. I used to travel regularly when I played tennis. I trained and played tournaments in France, Spain, Germany and the USA. I miss that. I know Africa is hardly the same. It's not so starry and we certainly won't be going from one smart hotel with a gym, swimming pool and line of tennis courts to another. But Africa will be more interesting and I'm going to see more than a hotel room. I have pictures in my mind of the wild African bush, the workers, the verandah where Gerald and Margaret drank their sun-downers, the crimson sunsets, the flat-topped hills, the rough roads and terracotta-coloured tracks, the tropical heat, the giraffes and the elephants, the kudu, the dust and the rain. The snakes.

I slot a new tape into the dictaphone and wait restlessly.

Come on. Where is Granny?

'Here she is!' Mum says, bringing Granny into my room. She has just been to the hairdressers to have a perm.

After a round of compliments about Granny's hair we get started. 'After our six month trip around southern Africa, we knew we wanted to go. We couldn't wait to build our house and start the farm work,' Granny explains. 'There was so much to do! It was too exciting for words. But first we had to gather ourselves in England. I wanted to learn how to drive and I needed to go to a cooking school. You see, I couldn't even boil an egg!' she rocks forward, still keeping her arms crossed firmly. I laugh and she laughs after me. It is one of her short laughs, it's more like a little yelp. Then, quickly, she looks quite serious again. 'The only thing I'd ever made was fudge!' she says, followed by another quick crow of incredulity.

I was like that. My poor uncle would receive vanilla fudge in a makeshift box every Christmas, without fail. If I felt adventurous I would put sultanas into the recipe too. He must have been dying to throw the box on the floor and scream, 'Not again!'

'I caught the bus to High Street Kensington with Mary.'

'What sort of things did you learn to make?'

'Mousses.'

I wait for more. 'Is that all?' I finally ask.

'Apple tart.' There's another pause. 'We were pretty hopeless, especially the American girl.'

July 1925

'Hands up who can boil an egg?' the teacher asked.

Twelve sets of eyes stared at her. Eventually two hands

wobbled up in the air without much conviction.

The teacher smiled, rubbing chubby hands together. 'Don't look so worried girls. By the end of three weeks, you will all be able to read and work from a cookery book and prepare basic meals. Right, we are going to make a salad first.' She handed out ingredients. Everyone had a lettuce, a few tomatoes and a cucumber on their work table. They were instructed to wash the lettuce first. The girls turned to their sinks and taps were turned on. Decked in gold jewellery, Margaret's pin-sized American neighbour, Elsie, hummed as she washed each leaf individually with soap and water.

By the end of the course the girls knew one another well. They were all close in age and had a lot in common. While chocolate and sponge cakes were baking slowly in the ovens, they talked. Two of them were going to start a cake shop serving home-made teas. They were a quiet serious pair. Elsie was learning to cook for her husband. Most of them were learning to cook before their weddings.

Margaret told the girls that she was going to Africa and although she would have an African cook in the future, she would have to teach him from scratch.

'Why are you going to Africa, darling?' asked an astonished Elsie in her southern drawl. 'Isn't it awfully primitive? What about the snakes and the wild beasts?'

Margaret told the others that she had already been on a six month trip around South Africa. She and Gerald wanted to go into farming.

'We were put on to the Settler's Association who help people like us emigrate,' she explained. 'They fixed our itinerary. We stayed with families in various districts to get an idea of their type of farming and the surrounding countryside.'

Margaret recalled her trip with enthusiasm. Her first sight of the Cape at sunrise; being struck by the pronounced South African accent; the natives begging for 'ticky' and bread on the trains, some of the children wearing nothing at all; the men wearing just a loin cloth of animal skin, topped by a straw or felt hat; going to Johannesburg; fishing on the Zambezi; seeing the mist above the Victoria Falls; visiting farms scattered all over the place – Durban, Grahamstown, Salisbury[1] and Bulawayo in Rhodesia.

'We dined out every day for the first four weeks, each farmer pushing hard for us to settle near them. But we did not want to be considered two suckers fit for an easy deal.' The others all laughed. 'We were given an introduction to a very rich man called Bailey who had made his money on Johannesburg gold and Kimberley diamonds and ostrich feathers. He asked us to lunch with him in his lovely villa in the Cape, but do you know,' she leaned in closer towards the girls in a hushed voice, 'he proved to be a very sexy old man. He played footsy with me under the table. Later he led me downstairs and tried to kiss me.' There were shocked gasps. 'I was so angry, I slapped his face. He then had the audacity to give me a feather fan! Gerald was so incensed that he made me give it away, it was a horrible fan. We didn't go and see him again.'

Elsie clapped her hands in admiration. 'What an adventure, petal,' she said.

'Yes, a real adventure. We're going to settle in Durban, go into sheep farming,' she stated proudly. 'In fact our visit to Durban coincided with the Prince of Wales who was on tour

---

[1] Harare

in South Africa. A big dance was laid on for him to which we were invited.' She did not know that providence was to step in and change their plans.

'Time to take the cakes out now,' the teacher instructed as she looked at her wrist watch. Margaret's looked more like a flat tyre as she'd forgotten to add the baking powder. Elsie laughed at hers. She had forgotten to turn on the oven.

Next Margaret was going to learn how to drive.

Dickie, the driving instructor from the London School of Motoring, wound the handle in the front of the car. Margaret sat watching. A red bus hurtled past, passengers sitting on the top layer with rugs around them, shivering in the wind. Margaret loved catching the bus, you could travel for miles for just a penny. Yet she longed to drive like Gerald and knew that it would be a help for him in Africa. Gerald had got rid of the Buick; now they had a white Standard car.

'I hope it doesn't rain, Lady Margaret,' Dickie smiled as he jumped into the passenger seat, 'we don't want to get wet.'

He was a tiny man, whose thin legs hardly reached the floor of the car. He wore a tweed cap and Margaret noticed how dirty his fingernails were.

'Just put your foot on the accelerator, it's as simple as that,' he said.

'Here we go!' Margaret had the whole road to herself. There was little traffic as they drove up High Street Kensington. 'Isn't this wonderful?' Margaret shouted. It was hard to hear herself over the noise of the car.

'You're a natural, Lady Margaret,' Dickie praised.

'Then the time came to say goodbye. I'm afraid my mother was in tears,' Granny says gently, her voice quietening.

'I'm not surprised. They didn't know when they were going to see you again.'

'That's right. The worst part of going overseas was saying goodbye to relations, friends, my grandmother.'

January 1926

Grandmother Balfour sat in her chair in her drawing-room wearing an odd hat and one of her long black tight-fitting suits with narrow white lace edging the high neck-band. The black looked severe set against her silvery white hair. Margaret sat quietly, hoping to get the goodbyes over and done with. Her grandmother grew more senile by the day. For the last ten years her mind had slowly deteriorated.

Margaret thought it pointless trying to tell her about the decision to go to Africa. She would not take it in. Still, Mother had to try. 'Margaret is going to South Africa to live, so she has come to say goodbye mother.'

Granny stirred from the chair and looked directly at her daughter. 'Julian, dear, you'll mind that terribly won't you.'

Margaret and her mother looked at each other with mouths wide open. Julian smiled back at her with pride.

'Yes, I will miss her dreadfully.'

2 February 1926

Barty was with his mother and father outside their London house, ready to wave Margaret and Gerald goodbye. Gerald watched him. He knew Barty and Margaret had a special bond, ever since they were children. Barty was fourteen months older than Margaret and, as a baby, it was feared he might have rickets. The doctors had said that he would never be able to go to school.

'I wouldn't have any of it,' Margaret had told Gerald. 'I was determined to build up his strength and nurse him back to health. He longed to play cricket and go to school like any other normal child and I so wanted it for him too.' Gerald had smiled when she described how she used to feed Barty bread, butter and jam sandwiches or freshly made scones which she had stolen from the still room when the maids' backs were turned.

Margaret had told Gerald that she and Barty had worked on the tree house together, stealing bits of wood and tools from the house carpenter to build furniture to sit on. They made it their secret hiding-place and called it 'The Fort'. When cousins came to stay, he and Margaret would ask them sweetly if they wanted to play in the tree house. Would they like to see the latest chair they had made? Barty climbed up first, Margaret following, holding on to the rope ladder and his weak legs to make sure he didn't fall. 'When we reached the top we snatched the rope ladder away so the cousins couldn't reach us,' Margaret had laughed wickedly. 'We found Rosemary Wilbraham especially trying as she was a Londoner and not used to country pursuits.'

Gerald had laughed, saying she and Barty sounded like little monsters. 'I suppose we were!' Margaret laughed back.

Gerald remembered her saying that Barty had to lie down and rest in the early afternoon. At bedtime she would watch Nanny Liza strap his legs into leather splints, worried that the heavy straps might hurt him.

Gerald looked at Barty. No one would think he had suffered, he thought. Barty reminded him of Margaret in looks. They could almost be twins. Both dark with fine features, there was a gentleness about him and yet he was such a strong spirited man. He wasn't particularly tall, but he was well built and proportioned. Together, Margaret and Barty had proved the doctors wrong because he did go to prep school and Harrow, and then on to Magdalen College, Oxford where he became the first Harrovian to win a rugger blue.

'I love you, please be careful Marka,' Barty said quietly, bowing his head so as not to show his tears.

Gerald watched her as she touched his hand and then moved towards her parents. While Margaret and her mother exchanged tearful goodbyes Margaret's father said, somewhat stiffly, to Gerald, 'Good luck and please take care of her.'

Gerald sensed that what he wanted to say was, 'I'll never forgive you should something happen to her.'

'I shall write, every week,' he overheard Margaret reassuring her mother. 'I will let you know how we all are, especially Anne.' Anne was coming up to two years old and was sleeping peacefully, oblivious to the occasion. Gerald was envious. Any kind of goodbye rattled him, his shoes were tapping down restlessly on the pavement.

'We must go,' he said to Margaret.

They needed to go before any minds were changed.

CHAPTER NINE

I am sitting in my doctor's surgery, waiting to be seen. My ankle hurts. Mum, Aunt Diana and I are meant to be leaving for Zimbabwe on 31 January, three weeks from now, for our six-week trip. The flights are booked. Yet there is something in the air telling us not to go.

Mum asked Aunt Diana if she wanted to come with us a few months ago.

Aunt Diana is the second eldest of Mum's sisters, born in October, 1927, three and a half years after Anne. Mum does not feel able to take me on my own. 'If you feel unwell I'll need help. Besides, it will be lovely to have Diana with us. She is longing to go back to our old home, she hasn't been back for fifty years,' she reasoned.

I wasn't going to argue. Annoyingly I could see Mum's point of view.

However, the idea of going on holiday with my mother and an aunt whom I didn't know particularly well made me feel suddenly depressed and aware of my situation.

I would love to be able to backpack around the country with friends. None of my friends go on holiday with their Mums and aunts, do they?

'Alice, would you like to come in,' my doctor asks as he walks into the waiting room. I gingerly get up and hobble behind him. I am sure he will tell me it is an insane idea to go. Look at me! I can hardly walk.

He asks me how it's going.

'It's terrible. I haven't been able to walk properly for nearly ten days.' I tell him that the pain started on Christmas Eve.

He holds my foot gently and asks me to point to where it hurts. 'When are you going to Zimbabwe?'

'In three weeks,' I reply tentatively. This is it, he's about to shake his head.

'Right, that gives us time to order you a splint.' He opens his drawer and takes out a catalogue. He points to a picture on the page. 'You need this strong multi-coloured support.'

I stare at him.

'You must go,' he says, 'just be careful to pace yourself.' He looks down at my feet, 'What have you got to wear shoe-wise?'

'Trainers or sandals. I've got my big clumpy black DM type boots which I had specially made by Bill Bird.' Because I find it so difficult to buy shoes, I had a pair of leather boots hand-made to mould around the shape of my feet. Bill Bird has a workshop in Gloucestershire, near to where Granny lives. He makes Granny's shoes too; it's hard to know which is the left one or the right one. I can't tell you how I felt writing out a cheque for £600 and being presented with a pair of beautifully made yet wonky-looking boots. I kept on thinking that I could have bought three pairs of Jimmy Choos. Still, they are comfortable and Mum tells me that they have 'great charm'. She calls them my friendly boots. 'I don't think they're really summer shoes though,' I conclude.

'Wear the boots and have a good time.'

'You really think I can go like this?' I think the tiny scared part of me wants him to say, 'Don't go. Rest and watch videos.' The new series of Friends must be coming out soon?

'I'm actually just as worried about the political situation in

79

Zimbabwe. You're going at a troubled time.'

'I know. I'm not sure we should go.' I'm letting the insecure part of me talk again.

'Look, go. I know you'll be sensible. Wear the splint every-day, pace yourself, and don't forget to send me a postcard,' he finishes with a wry smile.

My doctor knows about the Africa project. I told him that we were going to stay at Granny's old farm near Bulawayo, Zimbabwe. He is right – Zimbabwe has been increasingly on the news. The economic situation is deteriorating and people are losing what little faith they had in President Robert Mugabe's government. There are rumours that we won't be able to get petrol. Transactions are being handled by a government agency so heavily in debt to the oil companies, that they have stopped supplying them. The latest report, which is confusing, says that it is diesel which is short in supply and we have been assured our Mazda 626 runs on petrol.

More worrying still are the rumblings that Mugabe is threatening to invade and take over the white farmers' land. We would be spending the majority of the time at M'Coben with Fred and Betty Duckworth. They are bravely having us to stay on and off for three weeks. Fred's mother and father bought the farm from my grandparents. When Fred's parents died it ceased to become a working farm. Fred and Betty had full-time jobs working from M'Coben for the local Council. However, they have kept a small dairy farm. In these kinds of situations I am a strong believer in fate. I had started to think that someone was telling us not to go.

Mum rang Aunt Diana over Christmas to warn her about the pain in my ankle. 'I can think about painting the sitting room instead,' Diana said, trying to disguise her disappointment.

'Aunt Diana's being very good about it,' Mum told me.

However, my doctor is saying GO. Mum and I talk about it on the way back in the car. We don't know what to do.

In the morning we ring Aunt Diana. The time has come to make up our minds.

'We want to go,' Mum tells Diana on the phone. 'Alice isn't great but we'll take the wheelchair. If there are any problems we will cope.'

'Are you sure?' I can overhear Diana ask in a deeply surprised but excited tone.

'Yes, positive,' Mum smiles as she looks over at me. 'Dig out your passport again.'

I watch passengers file past, cramming their luggage into the overhead lockers and taking their seats. I am sitting in the front, in a row of seats with more leg space. One of the few advantages of having rheumatoid arthritis is being allocated better tickets.

I overhear a conversation in the seat behind me. 'Have you been to Africa before?' a girl asks. She has sat herself next to a rather handsome dark-haired man.

'No, first time,' the man replies.

I can sense her eyes light up as she says, 'You will love it. Africa gets into your soul.'

I had asked Granny, just before we left, if she would like to return to Africa. Without any hesitation she had answered, 'No, I would find it too sad. So much has happened since I was there. It's not the Rhodesia I knew and grew to love.'

I found it hard to relate to her sadness. To me, going out to Africa and seeing her old home is one big adventure, just as it had been for Granny at the beginning. I cannot imagine that I will be disappointed because everything is new, although it is another story for Mum and Aunt Diana.

Eventually I spot Mum behind a woman with a pink bobble hat carrying a BHS bag. 'There she is!' Mum says smiling. Everyone can hear her. For a moment I feel like the twelve year old girl who used to tell Mum to keep her voice down when she took me to tennis tournaments. Mum, Diana and I were separated as I was taken to the boarding gate in a buggy in front of everyone else. Another advantage of having RA. I smile as I watch her walk towards me, laden with duty free bags, the gin and vodka bottles chinking together.

As the plane leaves the runway, the three of us have the same expression of incredulity on our faces – we are actually going. Mum and Diana must stop fearing that they might be making the biggest mistake in their lives in trying to unravel the past and retrace steps back to their old home after so many years.

For myself, OK, it might have been more normal travelling with a tall, dark-haired, handsome man who wouldn't think twice about giving me the window seat but I'm not and my mother is my best friend. I know we'll have fun together like we always do. It will be a chance to get to know Diana too. I tell myself to expel all negative thoughts. I will not contract malaria and die. My joints will not swell and 'flare-up' so that I have to be extricated from my seat and carried off the plane after the long ten-hour flight.

I had told the Sister who administered my injections that I was desperately worried about the long journey because it was something that I hadn't done in over ten years. The last long flight I went on was when I was fifteen. I went to America with Bill, my tennis coach, to play in various competitions in Florida. I won an international tournament in Miami, I reflect incredulously.

'Are you OK, Alice?' Mum asks, breaking my thoughts. 'Remember to keep walking up and down the plane.'

The Sister told me that I must walk up and down the length of the plane at least every half hour, and drink plenty of water, 'Try not to drink alcohol,' she advised. How dull...but then a flare-up is even duller.

I lean back and breathe deeply. We are all care-free, excited, relaxed and determined to enjoy ourselves.

'I don't know if I can take this,' Diana suddenly mutters quietly.

Mum and I turn to her in fear. I shouldn't have been thinking all the above positive thoughts. 'What's wrong?' I ask her.

She shakes her head. 'Ten hours.'

'Aunt Diana, what's wrong?'

'How am I going to last for ten hours without a fag?'

Now, that is a worry.

It's 3am. Mum's and Diana's eyes are shut but I'm not sure if they're really asleep. I am wondering how we will all get on during the course of the holiday. It will be an intense three-some. We won't be able to go off and do our own thing. We will be stuck together. I am relieved that Helen and James are coming out to join us halfway through the trip. I imagine the three of us will be quite stale in conversation by that stage. They are going to a wedding in Cape Town and will be with us for a week afterwards.

Diana and Mum are eleven years apart in age. Although I do not know Diana well, I am aware that they have always been close. 'You can't analyse it, it's just one of those things,' Mum told me.

Before we left, I asked Mum how Diana felt about going away with me. Apparently she said, 'Well what if I have a heart attack? You should be more concerned about taking an old Granny like me.' I liked that.

'She wants to get to know you. Diana knows the potential

difficulties we may face but she won't let anything stop her from going back home,' Mum replied. 'You see, it had never crossed her mind that she would ever go back to Africa. This is, realistically, her only chance to return.'

After we land, I shuffle down the steps, conscious that I am keeping a planeload of people waiting but determined not to worry about that any more. It's too bad. I'm just relieved that everything is going according to plan and flare-ups have been kept at bay. The signs are changing. Maybe fate is on my side after all. I asked for a wheelchair at Harare as my ankle is still sore and I am being extra cautious not to overdo it these first few days. As I reach the bottom of the steps a young man is standing with what looks like an old rusty pram rather than a wheelchair. He manoeuvres it towards me but the wheels clearly have a mind of their own. We make erratic progress across the tarmac to the airport building. The warm sunshine beams across my face. It's wonderful.

The first thing that strikes me is that time has no meaning here. We have been at the Eurocar hire office for over an hour. Diana looks desperately hot and tells me out of the corner of her mouth how she wishes she'd taken off her tights.

'Now the car takes petrol doesn't it?' Mum asks again.

'OK,' he grins widely as he looks into our frustrated faces.

'Do you have our mobile phone?' I ask him.

'OK,' he grins again as he shuffles the paperwork around. 'No problem.'

'Do you have a spare set of car keys?' Diana asks sensibly.

'Ah, no, you won't lose them,' he replies.

We shift uneasily. He obviously has no idea about us and keys.

Finally we have manipulated our mountain of luggage, wheelchair and all into the small boot of the car and we're ready to go. Before we drive to my grandparents' old home, M'Coben, near Bulawayo, we are staying overnight with friends called the Piercys who live on the outskirts of Harare. We set off gingerly, still unsure which button does what in the car. The windscreen wipers are unnecessarily on at full speed. Mum has a stick with a knobbed end lying down the side of the passenger seat, on standby to ward off any foes.

Diana peers at the map and predicts that the journey from Harare to Bulawayo will take close to six hours. Within forty-eight hours we will have travelled from England to M'Coben, incredible when I remember Granny telling me that, 'It was the most tedious journey, two and a half weeks on the Union Castle steam ship followed by two nights and three days on a train from Cape Town to Bulawayo. The children were always sick, and for two and a half weeks on that wretched boat, I did nothing but clean up after them.'

'I envy you Granny,' I replied. 'It must have been so exciting.'

'It was a terrific adventure.'

'It was brave of you to leave home.'

'No, it was nothing to do with being brave,' Granny shrugged. 'It was the beginning of a new life.'

A life that I am about to step into.

CHAPTER ELEVEN

We are driving back into Harare, having just spent a wonderful night with the Piercys. Their home is a dream. My bedroom was large and airy with wide windows and the garden crowding in, almost a part of the room too. *Vogue* and *Tatler* magazines were sitting on my bedside table making it impossible to get out of bed in the morning. As I curled up in the sheets I felt safe and warm. After the long journey this was just what I needed, my body returning to normal, almost as if I was in a decompression chamber. And we ate delicious fresh mango cut into immaculate slices for breakfast. It was hard to leave, especially after the Piercys gave us a few warnings about how to avoid disasters on and off the road:

Pay attention to other drivers – just because they indicate left does not mean they will actually turn left.

Don't listen if someone tells you that you have a puncture. One turn and your bag will be snatched.

Don't stop to go to a public loo, you will only get mugged.

Wind windows up and rely on air conditioning.

Don't ever drive with unlocked doors.

Don't ever pick anyone up.

What kind of a place are we in? I wanted to stay in my decompression chamber and carry on reading *Vogue* and *Tatler*.

It feels strange to be in Zimbabwe at last. People did tell me one of the first things I'd notice was being in the minority. I feel like our appearance screams, 'English alien people in posh hired car are here!' I have not spotted one white face yet. Diana tells us she feels slightly disappointed by Harare. 'It does not feel like we're in Africa. It's not the bush veldt.'

In the thick of the city traffic Diana has that stick on hand waiting for anyone who vaguely approaches our car. A newspaper boy is heading our way and I can see Diana clutching the knobbed end of the stick with extra force. We see a long queue for diesel. Thank God we are not in it.

We are now out of town and on a straight tarmac road to Bulawayo, the sign says three hundred and ninety six kilometres, roughly two hundred and fifty miles. We pass a mother walking barefoot with a baby strapped snugly on to her back along with what looks like a heavy bag of food on her head. Another girl carries a large barrel on her head. I wonder if it is good for them being weighed down with such heavy loads but their backs look surprisingly straight.

Occasionally a rickety blue and white bus passes us. When a lorry overtakes we hold our noses and shut our mouths as it belches out its smoky fumes. Other than that there is refreshingly little traffic on the roads. The life is on the roadsides where people are selling fresh fruit, baskets, tall giraffes and other wood carvings. We see a number of people trying to sell worms which must be a meagre living.

We are over half way there. I realise too late that you have to pee at any given opportunity and I missed my chance at the café where we had lunch. We pull over to the side of the road. Mentally I run through the things Helen told me to take into consideration in this situation:

Spiky grass

Camouflaged snakes

Ants (especially if they fly)

Curious onlookers

Oncoming vehicles.

And then the Piercys also told us to pee in a bush but search your bottom and legs for ticks afterwards, I think to myself as I get out of the car.

After five hours driving on straight roads, the only hazard being potholes which you swerve to avoid, we are nearly there. We are just beyond Bulawayo, a small town where Margaret and Gerald started their journey that very first time when Granny went to see their future home. 'I had never seen the land,' Granny explained, 'Gerald had left me for ten days at Durban, where we had originally planned to settle, and returned from his trip like an excited child dying to share his news. He had stayed with people called the Binghams, near Bulawayo, and had taken out an option on 2,500 acres of their property. "The soil is rich, we could grow oranges, maize, tobacco and cotton," he told me. "Tobacco grows well out there. There is also a perfect site for the house with a permanently running stream on our boundary." I had taken a natural instinct against Rhodesia because the countryside was ugly and unfashionable, but when Gerald told me he had managed to buy the land for £1 per acre when the asking price was £2, this wasn't something I could sniff at.'

As we are driving I try to picture what that day must have been like. It's hard considering the road we travel on is dead straight and the journey from Bulawayo to M'Coben will take us forty minutes. It took Margaret and Gerald six hours. However, the countryside hasn't changed dramatically. It is just as Granny described – full of thorny bushes, small trees and in the distance these curious flat-topped hills which Diana tells me are called 'Kopjes'. 'It's a Dutch word,' she says.

Granny told me she was anxious to see the property for the first time, 'I had lost my voice after the long journey and had to be quietly patient until Gerald motored me out. I barely slept a wink the night before, I was longing for the morning to arrive.'

June 1926

Margaret and Gerald left the Bulawayo Country Club, a rather second-rate private hotel, at sunrise, capturing the magical shards of pink and gold of the sun just before it came up. They had bought an axe and spade for the journey and hired a native boy called James to help them make their way through the veldt.

Margaret wore a blue cotton frock with a felt hat and Gerald wore a pair of khaki knee-length shorts, topi and a white short-sleeved shirt. They set off in the Armstrong Siddeley that Gerald had been particularly proud to hear was the first model in the Bulawayo district and possibly in the whole of Rhodesia. The car had no roof or sides, just a canvas hood sheltering them from the sun. They had a blueprint map of the area they were to settle. Some vague markings of native kraals and paths were supposed to tell them how to reach the property. Even though Gerald had visited the farm already, he could quite foresee them getting lost without James to help them find the way.

Gerald had warned Margaret that outside the town the road was little more than a rough track. To Margaret's disbelief, it was no wider than a path and somehow far worse than she had imagined. They bumped along the Umguza valley track some thirteen miles or so, Margaret taking in the surrounding countryside. The land was a vast plateau and mainly flat, broken here and there by curious flat-topped hills. The trees also looked as if they had had their tops shaved off. There was not much to see but endless thorn-bushes which James told them were called, 'Mopani' bushes. It was very different to her home in England, with its cultivated gardens, clipped hedges and neat boundaries.

The car pulled to a halt as they reached the first drift across the Umguza River. The drift was badly paved with rough stones, the stream flowing strong, at least nine inches deep. Margaret glanced anxiously at Gerald. She watched him press his foot hard down on the accelerator and, looking straight ahead, he powered the car through the water, safely to the other side.

We approach and glide over the first bridge across the Umguza. Instead of the roller-coaster down to the bridge and up again, a new bridge has been constructed much higher off the river, making it far less dramatic. Diana and Mum say it has changed so much that it is disappointing not to recognise anything. 'The approach and exit from the drift used to be quite hazardous,' Mum says. We move on, until we reach the Hilda's Kraal Road.

Having travelled some thirty miles the road petered out leaving a narrow poorly marked track. For the next few miles the car frequently stopped and started, each time Gerald and James jumping out with the axe and spade to chop down the bushes obstructing their way.

'Hilda's Kraal,' James pointed out, as they came to a large clearing.

'I have it on the map,' exclaimed Margaret excitedly. They must be quite near now.

Margaret was jigging up and down on her seat with one hand holding on to her felt hat. In her opinion, Gerald drove rather too fast. They were travelling at well over twenty miles per hour. 'We must be nearly there!' she called out in frustration to him.

Women! Gerald thought to himself. So damn impatient. 'Nearly,' he called back.

'We must be nearly there?' I frown.

Aunt Diana takes an extra strong drag on her cigarette before stubbing it out. 'Nearly,' she mutters. We pass a bottle store, a few shacks and shops as we approach the left hand turn to Hilda's Kraal. We find ourselves on an excellent tarmac road that has recently been built to connect the Falls and Nyamandhlovu road.

Nyamandhlovu was a very small railway town where heavy baggage, parcels of food and mail were collected. I ask them if they recognise where they are,

'Not yet,' they both reply in unison. 'I think this must be the old rough track to Nyamandhlovu. You have to remember it's fifty-one years since I've been back,' Diana reminds me in a plodding tone. I have a feeling I'm going to be reminded too often.

'This road is unrecognisable anyway, Alice,' Mum plods on. 'When we were here it was deep in dust. It was no more than a dirt track.'

School children and mothers emerge from the long thatching grass that borders the edge of the road. There are no buildings in sight, just vast stretches of road ahead of them. Where are they going? A small boy waves at me and I wave back. He grins broadly, giggles and runs to catch up with his friends. The women wear bright raspberry, orange and lime colours with kerchiefs in their hair. Mum is right. I should not wear so much black. It takes only minutes to get to 'Content Road' which is the turning for M'Coben. There is another large sign which says, 'F. Duckworth. M'Coben. 4 km.'

Diana lights up another cigarette, her hand shaking, and winds down the window. She can hardly breathe. Mum inhales deeply. I suppose they can't help themselves wondering again if they are doing the right thing coming back, that it might be a terrible mistake. Will it be an anti-climax? Will it tarnish the memories of their childhood because everything has changed beyond recognition? Diana straightens up as if to say, 'Steady, pull yourself together, woman, it will hardly do to arrive in a complete state of collapse.'

The road is more like a track but still wonderfully accessible compared to how it must have been in Granny's day. The soil is a deep terracotta red colour. We pass what look like a few farm buildings on the right and a weary woman walking on the side of the road in downtrodden black plimsolls and a cotton skirt which looks more like an apron. They must get tired from all the walking.

'Do you recognise this?' I ask hopefully as I look out of the window. By now they must do, surely?

'No,' they both smile nervously, 'not yet.'

Why don't they recognise where we are? We are so close now. I know it's been fifty years but this is unbelievable. It can't have changed that much. Or maybe we are in the wrong place? It is hard to accept that there is a house at the end of the road. We are in the middle of nowhere. As we continue there are still no murmurs of recognition. Maybe we took the wrong track and are now heading off to Mugabe's home? Diana spots a beautiful heron and immediately looks through her binoculars. I want to move on.

We come to a part which forks into two tracks but joins up again fairly quickly. We opt for the less steep of the two.

It is not until we reach what Diana and Mum call, 'their drift' that the atmosphere in the car changes. Choked with surprise, Mum's voice breaks the silence, 'Look, the Mpandeni stream has completely dried up.' I learn that the Mpandeni was their favourite fishing spot. Now it is dusty and overgrown with trees.

Diana looks disappointed. 'Before there was no bridge like this. The car would bump over boulders through the water and then it had to rev up to reach the top of the hill on the other side,' she says nostalgically, swooping the action with her arms and hands. 'The rainy spells did not last for more than ten days, but during that time our small river became a wide torrent,' Granny had said. 'It was impossible to cross by car. The black soil on the far side of our "drift" became so muddy that it took four or six oxen to drag a car through. It was impassable when the water was in full flood.'

They reached the Mpandeni stream which marked the boundary to their land. There was no ready-made crossing. After instructions from Gerald, acted out like a charade as he had no idea how to speak Ndebele, James jumped out and set to work. Margaret noticed his shoestring-thin legs. As he bent over however she could see that his back was remarkably broad and well muscled.

He and Gerald dug away at the bank so as to allow the car to cross the river and mount the steep bank on the far side. The river was only a few yards wide but running strongly, opening out into large pools both above and below them. Gerald was sure there could be a few crocodiles lurking nearby. The sun was beating down on both their backs. Margaret could see a long sticky line of sweat on Gerald's shirt. They began to descend the steep bank and the car jolted against a large stone. Gerald changed into a lower gear and heard the engine churn in protest. 'Blast it,' he cursed under his breath. As they edged up the bank, the wheels crunching against the stones, Margaret held her breath, sure that they were going to slide back down again. Gerald pushed hard down on the accelerator and after a mighty rev they made it to the other side.

'That was splendid, splendid! Well done darling,' Margaret cheered loudly. To her immense relief a clear, albeit bumpy, track led away from the stream ahead of them.

'Not far now,' Gerald said, full of eager anticipation. Margaret smiled back, trying to keep calm. She felt faintly sick with apprehension, praying she was going to like this place as much as Gerald did.

'Still, I prefer driving on these roads than driving on the M25!' Diana remarks as we turn another corner.

'I think I'm going to be sick,' Mum says. She winds down the window. 'I can't believe I'm here.'

'Are you OK?' I ask her. Diana puts the hand-brake on and I can see she is crying. After a long emotional pause and the wiping of tears Mum finally says, 'Come on, let's move on.'

Diana says that if this moment was set to music there would be a passage of mounting crescendo, ending with a dramatic chord as the house comes into view, and then silence.

As we approach the house a high security fence tells us how times have changed. In Mum and Diana's day the only room they locked was the storeroom where bags of sugar and other groceries wouldn't stand a chance of remaining on their shelf. The old front of the house looks just as it did before except that the door has been bricked up. 'That was where our drive was,' Mum tells me pointing to what is now a side garden with citrus fruit trees and flowering shrubs.

'Oh look, the jacaranda trees are still there Pam,' says Diana emotionally. 'And the acacia trees.'

One of the workers in blue overalls opens the security gate and we park at the back of the house. The house is white-washed and thatched. There are a few garages with old cars, a tractor and a Toyota. It looks untidy and unfamiliar to Mum and Diana.

'It is Pamela,' says the man who opened the gate. He is walking towards us.

Mum looks delighted to have been recognised. She closely looks into his face trying to remember his name. 'It can't be Paul, is it? Paul?' she guesses. He grins widely, revealing only two teeth, and they clamp their hands together in the traditional Matabele three-times handshake. I watch Mum, unable to take her eyes away from him for fear that she might be imagining the whole encounter. 'Paul used to be our gardener,' she says, her voice flooded with emotion as she finally looks at me. 'The last time you saw me, I was thirteen,' she states incredulously, quickly turning back to Paul, her eyes wide with astonishment. 'I cannot believe you remember me. How old are you, Paul?'

'I don't know,' he laughs and Mum laughs back. 'I think we must be about the same age,' she smiles.

'The Ding-ding tree is just how I remembered it,' says Diana. 'I remember Anne and me standing here and feeding the baby reed buck. It must be at least one hundred years old,' she calculates in amazement.

The Ding-ding tree was the nick-name they used for the large mimosa tree because it used to have a long metal rod attached to one of the branches which was struck every morning at 'sun-up' by the house-boy to call the men to work. It is a great towering tree with a dark trunk.

Mum quickly points out to me the mimosa trees to the side of the house, 'That's the spot where Granny first camped. It feels strange being back. It feels like I've come home.'

I try to imagine M'Coben with no buildings or markings. It was a vast stretch of land with a few trees and huts. I try to see it just as Margaret did.

Gerald and Margaret continued another mile until they reached a clump of big mimosa trees, near to a few derelict-looking native huts and decided this was where they would disembark, leaving the car in the shade. Margaret clambered out and stretched her legs. She took in the surroundings.

There was little to see but a mass of thorn bush, spiky grass and stretches of undeveloped land ahead. Nothing seemed to lead anywhere. At home the land was cared for and farmed. Africa was an untamed wilderness.

For a brief moment Margaret felt daunted by the prospect of living in the middle of the bush. She knew that they were going to be starting from scratch, but it was only when she took in the sight before her that she truly comprehended what this move meant. Was she going to be lonely? There were not going to be any possible means of communication except for the few scattered neighbours, the nearest four miles away.

Yet at the same time Margaret was invigorated by the challenge. She was already looking forward to writing home to tell her mother about their future home.

A pair of black Ridgeback/Labrador/not-sure-quite-what's scamper out to meet us along with the Duckworths, Fred and Betty, two small, round figures. We hug and tell them about our journey.

'We're here Granny,' I say quietly as we walk inside.

CHAPTER TWELVE

Mum and I are sleeping in one of the small bedrooms that was part of the original three-bedroom cottage. 'It was a funny little house, just small square rooms,' Granny had told me, 'No ceilings, whitewash walls, open fires but no decorations and very plain doors.' Diana is sleeping in her parents' old bedroom that formed part of the extension they added to the house in 1930. The house is L-shaped with the added dining room, sitting room, bedroom and bathroom as well as a room that Fred and Betty now use as their office.

As I get changed it feels wonderful looking out on to the front verandah with the view of the flat-topped Turk Mine Hills. Wonderful in that Granny and I have talked so much about her home and now here I am, standing in the spot where she stood, looking at the same view she saw. I also feel as if I have been here for a long time because it already feels like home. When I woke up this morning, I knew exactly where I was. Often when you are in a strange place you can wake up and feel disorientated before you finally realise where you are. Nothing seems alien or out of place here. Perhaps this is because Granny described M'Coben so vividly that I felt I knew it already.

'Our old swimming-pool is long gone,' Mum says, pointing to the front of the lawn where it used to be. 'Gerald built the pool much later on,' Granny had told me during one of our recording sessions. 'A hole was dug by hand, he covered it in tarpaulin and made it out of concrete. We had to put chlorine in it to keep it nice and clean. I swam every day.'

'Our old pool used to be a sludgy green colour, like pea soup,' Mum laughs, 'Richard and I played endless games in it but I don't remember Mum swimming in it at all, it was probably too disgusting.'

Fred and Betty have also removed the low verandah wall so that you step right out on to the lawn. I was expecting a verandah wall because Granny described the time when Diana fell off it. 'I was lucky my Gerald was such a calm person,' she commented. I shouted for him, "Darling, Diana has fallen off the wall!" I was terrified she had hurt herself you see. Without any trace of anxiety Gerald shrugged and replied, "I knew it would happen one day but drunk men and babies rarely hurt themselves. She'll be fine." Sure enough Diana was none the worse for her tumble, Gerald was right!' she exclaimed cheerfully.

I look over to Mum who is now thinking how she would love to get her hands on the curtains and lampshades and give them a new lease of life. I can tell, she has that look about her.

The Duckworths are at home today, but tell us that they will be out for two days this week as Fred has bad neck problems and sees a physiotherapist in Bulawayo. We decide that we must wait until they've gone before we start striding round the house, pointing out improvements or things we don't like as much. When we were in the sitting room last night drinking vodkas and tonics, with the feeble excuse that the quinine should keep those mosquitoes away, I asked Mum and Diana if the house had changed much. They both said it felt very familiar and yet strange at the same time. Diana said she had to keep on pinching her arm to remind herself that this was the house she was brought up in. This was where she played with her toys; where she crawled around the verandah on her bottom; where she swam in the waterfall pool and little pools higher upstream the Mpandeni. 'The little pools were dry ninety-eight percent of the time and did not harbour the snails that carry bilharzia,' Diana said. The newer sitting room that was built later on in 1930 has barely altered. It still has the original black and white floor like a chess board, the brick fireplace, even the same bookshelves that line one side of the wall. 'We are putting in a big bookcase and it now only needs painting pale yellow. It is made up of five shelves with three cupboards at the bottom. Quite a work of art for Gerald to have carpentered!' Betty tells me that half the books are Margaret's old books. Margaret's and Gerald's desks are still there. Granny said, 'I went down to Cape Town in 1931 and bought this very lovely stinkwood furniture from an auction. My desk was dark like mahogany.' I sit down at Granny's desk and take myself back to all the letters I have read over the last six months. I am going to continue reading them here.

The only major change is that there are now two big french windows at the end of the room instead of the smaller original windows. These windows look out on to a new thatched shelter where Betty and Fred drink their tea or have a 'brai'. 'A what?' Mum asked. Fred laughed. 'What you folks call a barbecue,' he smiled. To the right of the thatched shelter is the clump of mimosa trees where Margaret and Gerald first camped.

Over supper last night, Mum told Fred that Granny had described his background. We were aware that he was born in Hong Kong and that he had been put into a prisoner-of-war camp by the Japanese during the Second World War with his mother, father and sister. He was thirteen at the time. His family were imprisoned for four years but miraculously they all survived. Fred was clearly reluctant to speak about his memories. The only thing Mum asked him clumsily was if being in camp was like the television programme, 'Tenko'. He paused for a moment and then, gently, he said, 'Yes, exactly like it.'

Betty, his wife, is a Scotswoman, with a Scots accent that seems a bit peculiar and rather funny since she has lived out here for over forty years. She used to be a nurse in Glasgow, where she met Fred. He still calls her, 'Lennox' because when they first met she was introduced to him as, 'Nurse Lennox'. Betty and Fred obviously have a mutual love of music because CD's were being played last night and are back on this morning. At one point during supper I thought I was going to turn into Kate Winslet when the music from Titanic was played for the third time. Worse things could happen. They also love music from the fifties and sixties which drives me mad, although I am outnumbered here.

'Oh I love the music to Salad Days,' Mum sighed.

'I haven't listened to Victor Silvester in a long time,' Diana hummed.

'Some enchanted evening,' Mum started to sing along flatly to the words of South Pacific.

Fred and Betty have arranged for Ambrose, one of the older farm workers, to take us on a drive up to the top of the kopje. This is where Margaret and Gerald planned to build their home during their first visit. Ambrose is usually found by the gates at the back of the house, near the garages, scything the grass in his ripped blue dungarees and brown felt boots.

As we approach him he smiles, revealing a set of enormous yellow teeth. He has a lovely round face with round cheeks. His English isn't too good, but he understands what we are asking and nods enthusiastically. We go back to our rooms to fetch sun hats and cameras and Diana still clutches the knobbed stick.

Ambrose helps me into the front of the old Toyota four-wheel drive, while Mum and Diana hop into the back. As Ambrose starts the car I feel slightly awkward in his company. Paul opens the security gate. Made of chain-link fencing wire, its metal uprights are curved at the top to carry three strands of barbed wire.

Last night, Diana told Fred and Betty she found it comforting to know that we are locked in at night. They laughed, 'Anyone can get over the gate in a twinkling,' Fred said. 'But it's better than nothing.' I pointed out that Fred's silver glittery toenails, which had been painted on by his grandchildren, would be enough to scare anyone off.

Ambrose sets off slowly and carefully. He drives like an old lady meandering on a Sunday, the kind of motorist we all dread being stuck behind. I sense that he doesn't get the chance to drive that much so he feels he must be extra cautious. I imagine it's a bit of a treat to be doing something other than scything the grass. Slowly, we pass an old rusty brown tractor and what could be an old tobacco barn on its very last legs. I imagine the barn was built by Gerald. When I think of the hard work and effort that Gerald put into building the barns, there is something depressing about their decay. It's sad to think that nothing new has replaced them.

As we are driving I ask Ambrose his age, something I later

learn I should not have done. Apparently you don't ask people their age if it is obvious that they are older than you. Oops. Ambrose tells me he was born in 1935, he has a wife and seven children.

'How often do you see your family?' I probe.

'One time a year,' he replies, looking a little crestfallen. He tells me he sees his wife for two weeks at Christmas.

'That's all!' I exclaim in disbelief. 'Are all your children born in September Ambrose?'

He looks lost, but laughs anyway. I don't think he really understands my unfunny joke and as I try to imagine the kind of life Ambrose must lead, I wish I had been more respectful. How miserable to see your wife and children only once a year.

Ambrose's driving is painfully slow. When going over rough rock he scrunches his eyes shut and hardly dares open them again until we're on smoother ground. Well, we're in no hurry. It's a lovely sunny day, pretty yellow and white butterflies flicker around us. I look out of the window, thinking that this is not a beautiful piece of countryside, it is very wild, with bushes of thorns and volcanic rock formations. Yet something in its lack of pretension and abandonment gives it life. Mum tells us she remembers these unusual rocks because she used to go riding with Granny up this hill, not only for exercise but to keep an eye on the workers in the cotton and maize lands[1] at the foot of the kopje. 'It was impossible to get a car up the kopje in our day, we always walked or rode,' Mum says.

Diana holds her binoculars to her eyes, she does not want to miss a single bird or creature. Diana is a garden designer and loves plants and wild-life. From a young age her interests have always centred on animals, birds and flowers. Granny

---

[1] Term used for fields which have been cleared of scrub and bushes

wrote to her mother that, 'She always points out a hornet in the room, or a big bird in the sky and of course the dogs and cats are her special friends. It's "look at the kitty-ga" or the "moo-ca".'

The kopje has an eerie feel to it. There are very few creatures and birds to be seen. No doubt the sound of the noisy engine has scared them away.

Ambrose's eyes are squeezed shut and squinting with pain as he tries to get the truck over a rough patch of rocks and further up the hill. We put him out of his misery by telling him we have come far enough. Besides, not one of us fancies getting stuck, especially not me.

'OK,' he agrees without hesitation. I ask him if we can just pause and take in the spectacular view. I have the exhilarating feeling that we are the only people alive. I can see exactly why Margaret and Gerald dreamt of building a house in this spot.

June 1926

Margaret and Gerald walked up a sandy track, hand in hand, and then came to the ridge of a hill, their boundary being a quarter of a mile further on. They began to tackle the rough climb. The great ironstone rocks looked volcanic. Even through their shoes they could feel the heat in the stone. A spring bubbled out of the side of the hill and ran down through a series of rock pools. They knew that the yellowing grass must hide plenty of snakes.

At the top of the hill they both leaned against a teak tree admiring the magnificent view over the valley. For a moment they were quiet. It seemed as if they were the only two people in the world. The view commanded some fifty miles of African bush country and, as Gerald had said, there was not one windmill nor building to be seen. There was only a line of those strange flat-topped hills. Gerald had always said that Rhodesia was not a beautiful scenic country, but a country of wide spaces, big views, and lovely sunshine. He was right and Margaret felt sure she would become attached to this place.

Gerald broke the silence with reality. 'The farm is absolutely bare veldt, no fences, buildings, nothing to speak of. It means a lot of hard work.'

Margaret brushed that concern to one side. 'It is far more satisfactory building a house from nothing. Starting from the very beginning.'

'I think it would be an idea to build our house here,' Gerald suggested, taking off his topi and putting an arm around Margaret.

'Yes, definitely an idea,' she replied.

She could picture their big house with an attractive rock garden. It was the perfect place for Gerald's shooting too, she contemplated happily, there must be plenty of guinea fowl, partridge, buck and other game on this hill. 'What is the native name of this place?'

Gerald had already done his research to impress her. 'M'Coben. It means, "Place of Ghosts".'

Margaret thought about the name for a moment.

'It's much better than Nyamandhlovu which means, "elephant's meat",' laughed Gerald, trying to persuade her to like it.

'Yes,' Margaret agreed. Although it appeared inappropriate to their youthful energy she did like it. 'M'Coben,' she repeated, 'Place of Ghosts. I love it.'

By the time Margaret and Gerald reached the dry spring at the foot of the hill they were famished and Gerald fetched the picnic from the car.

After eating they started inspecting more of the open country. 'The valley soil is wonderfully rich and fertile,' Gerald told her.

'Wonderfully rich,' Margaret agreed, 'well, look how high the grass is.'

Gerald walked Margaret down to the river. 'This is the Umguza which joins up with the spruit we crossed, the Mpandeni. I made Mr Bingham divide his farm in such a way that we have this river frontage of two and a half miles,' he explained, clearly delighted with his negotiating skills. The river banks were closely bushed and the grass grew to six feet or more. Camel-thorn and mimosa trees towered over the thorny bush. When Margaret looked behind her she wondered if they would find their way back. There were so few landmarks. However, they did finally manage to find the dry spring and the sandy track leading back to their car.

'Darling, I'm most impressed,' Margaret said as they walked arm in arm. 'You were clever finding it.'

They found James asleep under the shade of the mimosa tree. He opened his treacle-coloured eyes and jumped to his feet, brushing the ants off his legs.

They left, longing to begin the tough but irresistible process of taming the wild land.

Finally, Ambrose drops us off by the house. He comes over to my side and leads me by the arm to the back door. I am touched by his concern. He does not understand that I have

RA but he has a natural instinct to help.

'That's where the "cathedral" used to be,' Diana says as she hops out, pointing to the garage. The 'cathedral' was the nickname for the original boiler used for heating water for the bath. We thank Ambrose before going inside.

Mathanda, the Duckworths' main worker who cooks and looks after the house, makes us some tea. Mathanda comes into the room with a tea tray and puts it on the table without saying a word. I feel uncomfortable being waited on like this, I want to ask him to sit down with us. 'Thank you Matumba,' Mum says.

Fred laughs, saying 'Matumba' means 'bones' in Ndebele. He tells us Mathanda's wife lives here too, her name is Regina. I wait for Mum to get that one wrong. He also tells us that while we were out he found a baby four-foot python curled up like a pet in one of his filing cabinets. He chased it out only to find it had come back again, banging its body against the window.

'Where is it now?' I quaver.

Later, I am begging, 'Mum, can you check underneath my bed please,' as she is about to climb underneath her own mosquito net.

Mum lifts the covers and peers under the bed, 'You're in luck, no python tonight Alice,' she confirms.

I go to the bathroom to brush my teeth. Mum hears a scream and comes rushing out. Diana follows.

'What is it?' they shriek, just like Granny.

'Oh my God. There's a frog behind the door. It might even be a toad,' I say, hurt that they are laughing at me. 'It was huge and knobbly.' Fred told us that snakes creep in at night in search of frogs and toads so it is not good news to find one in the bathroom.

'You would be hopeless living out here,' Mum decides.

I have to admit she's right.

CHAPTER THIRTEEN

It's our second day and we are walking around M'Coben. Fred and Betty do not farm but keep cattle for milking. I feel as if I'm almost mirroring Granny's movements – driving out to their home for the first time, going up the kopje, and now exploring the farm. I am sitting under the mimosa trees, the very spot where Margaret and Gerald set up camp four weeks after their first visit. Granny described that first night. It sounded wonderful. They had visited the farm, chosen a site for the house and were both aching to get started. However, there was one major thing standing in their way. Money.

Gerald and Margaret had to wait to hear from Maynard, their lawyer in London, before they could start work on the farm. They had cabled the Trustees for £6,000 to buy the land and build the house. The money would come out of the Trust fund which had been set up by Margaret's family. The money was both Gerald's and Margaret's and could only be accessed with the permission of the Trustees who were a mixture of friends and family members.

Before they left London Maynard had assured them that they could withdraw up to £8,000 to invest in a property. This withdrawal would happen in the next few days and then they could start making plans.

Early June 1926

Gerald wanted to buy the oxen and farm implements. He wanted to tell the builder to start making the bricks. They would have to live in a tent, it would be uncomfortable but that didn't bother him, or Margaret. She had told him that there was so much to be done now that they had made the decision, that she was longing to get started.

For the moment, all Margaret could do was dream about their future home and write home describing what it would be like. 'We are going to have a big sitting room with a dining room divided off from it by a wide curtain. I shall have a big bedroom, with a big bathroom, store-room and Gerald's dressing-room opening out of it. There is going to be a big wide step all the way along the front and back of the house. I think we shall really be very comfortable and oh so happy.'

As Margaret sealed the letter, Gerald walked into the tent. His face was pale. 'I have just written to daddy. He was telling me about the coal strikes. I do wish we had some home papers to read,' she said. 'Gerald, what is wrong?'

Margaret read the cable slowly. The words were like stinging slaps in the face. 'The Trust does not allow money for building purposes nor does it allow buying land outside of England.'

She put her head into her hands. Maynard had assured Gerald in no uncertain terms that they could withdraw up to £8,000 to invest in a property. She could remember the exact wording, it was clause twenty-two,

'...the Trustees shall and they are hereby required to raise out of the Husband's Trust Fund or the Wife's Trust Fund or partly out of each any sum not exceeding Eight Thousand Pounds and invest the sum so raised in the purchase of and of making improvements in or on a dwelling house...'

When Gerald had asked Maynard if this clause held true for a property in Africa the answer had been a definite, 'Yes'.

Gerald put a hand on Margaret's shoulder.

'What are we going to do?' she whispered hopelessly. 'We have £1,500 saved up but that's not nearly enough to build a house. How can they do this?' Margaret was not only talking about Maynard but her Trustees.

Gerald read the last sentence of the cable out loud, 'Good luck but be very careful.'

'The brutes,' Margaret shouted. 'Who do they think they are! They are talking to us as if we are small children. "Be careful",' she mimicked their patronising tone. 'They are not our guardians. Gerald, we must cable back to say we abandon all claim to our,' she stressed the 'our' angrily, '*our* trust money.'

Gerald agreed. 'I have every intention of doing so. We will borrow the money. It just means going slow. We shall raise the money somehow,' Gerald vowed. 'They are not going to have their way.'

PS. 'Father, I had sealed this letter up. Now, we have just received a cable from the lawyer in London to say that the settlement does not allow money for building purposes, and he does not think it allows for buying land outside of England. We are dumbfounded. It has come as a hard blow, but we are determined to buy the farm. We shall have to go slow for many years and I am afraid your visit will have to be postponed for ages as we shall have to be content with huts now instead of a house.'

Ten days later

Their dreams had been shattered in one crippling blow. If they did take out a loan, the money would take a while to come through when every day was important. It was crucial to start and finish building before the rainy season in November. They were now well into June. The time the Trustees had wasted was infuriating. Margaret sat alone in the tent, and furiously started writing home,

'PRIVATE', she wrote and underlined in the top left hand corner. 'This letter is for you and Daddy. NOT for general publication.

My darling mother,

Since I wrote last week, we have been going through a very difficult time. All legal opinion here says we are entitled to our money and that if we had the funds we should perfectly be in our right to sue our Trustees. The leading lawyer in Bulawayo has practised in England for many years and he backs us up entirely in our claim.'

With each sentence she became more passionately convinced that it was her family's mistrust of Gerald that was the real cause of the decision. Margaret began to picture her family sitting at the table in the long parlour discussing, 'Margaret and Gerald's future'. She was imagining them mocking their ideas. 'Why the devil should they want to be stuck out in a wilderness, in a godforsaken country like Africa?' she could hear. 'Gerald should never have dragged our Margaret out there,' she heard again. Livid, Margaret started writing.

'If they think Gerald is fool enough to go headlong into buying land without legal opinion here, well – they must think it – that's all. But they must not expect us to be on friendly terms, because I will not stand having my husband insulted in this way.'

Margaret declared aloud, as if her family could hear her, 'We are determined to have the farm, we are going to borrow money and get it that way, it makes no difference what the Trustees say.'

She continued to write. 'It will mean we shall have to go very slow in the developing line, as with a borrowed millstone round our necks we can't do very much until the money is paid back. The house will have to go to the wall and we shall live in brick huts until we can afford something better. The thing that upsets me most is that Gerald should not be trusted. He does everything with a view to making a home for me, he has never made one move without consulting me, and together we have made the plunge – and then what does he get from my family? Nothing short of a blow in the face. Gerald knows how I feel about you all at home, and we are both deeply grieved and hurt that we have been met with such rebuff.'

She pictured her family shuffling their feet underneath the table and looking across at each other in shamed surprise. Margaret told herself to stop imagining. Her family were doing nothing of the sort, were they? This uneasy feeling would not leave her. If only she could be reassured that Mother and Father supported Gerald and her whole-heartedly in their venture. She would not hear for another six weeks. Six weeks. She hadn't realised quite how hard it was going to be feeling so far away.

'I do not know what attitude you and Daddy are taking up and I cannot know for another six weeks, but if you, too, feel like the Trustees, that Gerald cannot be trusted, my bitter cup will indeed be full...' She bit her lip and fought tears, 'and though it would break me in half to do it, I should never feel able to go home again – what has he done to deserve such treatment? Neither of us have been spendthrift or reckless and if people at home think that Gerald is rushing into buying land from sharks without going thoroughly into everything,

114

they are very much mistaken.' Margaret knew Gerald was acutely aware that he was mistrusted. She had seen it in his expression when he handed her the cable. 'Gerald feels these things very deeply, and time even won't wash them away. Whether a real apology would or not I cannot say. Oh Mother don't let us down, I don't think I could bear it – we didn't ask for anybody's money but our own, and we wouldn't accept anybody else's money. I know we can trust you and Daddy – you don't know how splendid Gerald is being so do trust us. All my love, Your very own little girl, Margaret.'

A week later another cable came from the Trustees laying down fresh conditions and saying the money might be forthcoming but as a loan and if they agreed to certain terms. Gerald had to laugh when he read them. 'One of the conditions is that we should pay back one tenth of the sum every year.'

'That's outrageous,' Margaret spat.

'The point is,' Gerald began, 'the Trustees are not legally allowed to lay down any of these rules. Either they can or they can't give us the money.'

'Imagine our friends or family planted down in huts with barely any money and told to get on with it,' Margaret said almost smiling because it was so absurd.

Gerald applied for a loan of £4,000 from a bank in England and they waited to hear. However, thanks to the generosity of Mr Bingham who said he didn't mind waiting for the money, they were back on track with their plans.

They had returned to M'Coben and walked around the land deciding that their idea of building a house on top of the hillside was naïve because it was far too rocky. They chose the site at the bottom of the hill near the mimosa trees where they had parked the car that first day. Their home would be much smaller but it would save them a lot of money.

Gerald had already made a rough design of the house to save the cost of employing an architect. As there was no drainage or water system to contend with for the moment, once they had built the kiln in which to make the bricks it meant straightforward building.

Their brick man was turning out to be a great success. Margaret loved watching him hard at work. When the old man really got going he could make four hundred daily. Gerald had bought a wagon, a two-wheeled scotch-cart and twenty head of oxen. They had bought all the necessary tools: a plough, picks and shovels. They had acquired a bell-tent and two corrugated iron huts which were now up and ready for them to camp in. They had procured their cook-boy George along with George's nephew, a fourteen year old piccanin[1] called Elardie, who would also be a house-boy.

Gerald had organised a water expert to come to the farm. This expert had told them the wonderful news that the spring below the house site would provide ample water for the house and garden. Not having to build a dam was going to be another money-saver.

Gerald was also absorbed in learning how to make tobacco, studying the process from start to finish. The land was going to be cleared of bush and divided up. He was planning to experiment on a small acreage to begin with as they could not afford to lose any money at this stage.

---

[1] Young boy

Margaret continued to write home. She prayed that she had their backing. 'It only goes to show so clearly that my Trustees do not trust my Gerald. I cannot get away from that fact and we both resent their attitude more than I can say. I do not jib at hardships, but I do kick at illegal things and they are treating us abominably.'

'I was wondering where you were,' Mum says as she sits down next to me. 'What are you doing?'

'Seething at the Trust letters. They were treated so badly.'

'Yes, so badly. I think the Trustees did behave outrageously. Mum doesn't talk about it now. She has never talked about it, to any of us.'

'Granny would not talk to me about it either. The only thing she did say was that the fault lay with the lawyer, Maynard. That's an easy person to blame though, isn't it?'

'That's right. The Trust business was the beginning of my father's life-long hatred of lawyers. What did she say about Maynard?'

'That he was double-faced. But I'm sure Granny knew it wasn't just Maynard's fault. It's the "Good luck but be very careful" which gives it away. She saw it as her family saying that Gerald was not good enough for her. In their eyes, Margaret should have made a titled marriage with a large and comfortable estate. Instead, they saw her struggling to make a miserable living in a mud shack surrounded by natives. If I felt my family didn't trust me,' I continue, 'I am sure I would have reacted in the same way. If I feel I have been treated badly I find it very hard to let go.'

'I know,' Mum agrees.

'I'd tell you to get stuffed.'

'You'd probably chuck me into the nearest lake.'

'Yes, I would!'

As I say this to Mum, I can't see the situation ever happening. But then I doubt Granny could have possibly imagined it would happen to her. If someone had told her before she set out for Africa that she would soon be threatening never to go back home, she would have laughed. 'Don't be so ridiculous,' she would have said. Yet when that moment of decision came, she stood up for Gerald and risked losing her family. That must have taken great courage.

The Trust business changed Granny, quite suddenly, from a young carefree girl into a passionate and wounded young woman. It made her even more determined to build their future at M'Coben. There was no way she was going to pack up their tents and come home at the first obstacle. Granny loved talking about their first night by the camping fire.

July 1926

Margaret and Gerald sat close to each other by the camp fire, enjoying the macaroni that George, the cook-boy, had prepared for them. 'My father didn't like the footmen wearing gloves when they served at the table,' Margaret smiled. 'He preferred to know their hands were clean.'

'We don't have to worry about that out here,' Gerald said with a large hint of relief as he congratulated George for managing to get the top so brown and crispy. George did speak English but was flummoxed by the word, 'crispy'.

They didn't have to worry about anyone else. Gerald was right. It was heavenly to be managing for themselves. The only person Margaret missed was Anne. She and Nanny were staying at the Country Club in Bulawayo. They would move out on to the farm when they were more settled.

Gerald held Margaret's hand. She moved closer to him. The moment the sun went down the temperatures dropped dramatically to near freezing. Margaret found it hard to believe they were settling in the tropics.

Margaret looked up into the sky. It was a brilliant cold starry night. Without a single glare from any city street lamp the stars seemed extraordinarily bright. Margaret thought the African sky had to be the largest sky in the world and it felt like she and Gerald had the sky and the stars all to themselves. 'I used to love sleeping on the roof at Longford,' she told Gerald. 'When we were little we used to tie each other down with dressing gown cords just in case we toppled over. There was something so lovely about being outdoors.' She turned to him.

'I know I am going to be so happy here, darling. We have a fire to keep us warm, the stars, our home.' She smiled. 'And a cook who has somehow managed to make the top of the macaroni crispy.'

'Thank you,' Gerald said quietly.

'For what?' Margaret whispered.

'For having faith in me.'

'She does have a strong sense of what is right and wrong,' Mum comments thoughtfully. 'She is fiercely loyal and fights for people she believes in. Like you Alice, she would always fight for you.'

'She's a good person to have on your side,' I smile. As Mum and I walk back to the house, Mum suddenly says, 'I'm sure you're right.'

'About what?'

'That the family felt he might not have been good enough,' she reflects sadly. 'If they did feel like this, they were so wrong. Gerald adored her and he did not let them intimidate him. I don't think he was daunted by her large family.'

We continue to walk. I lean on Mum's arm for support.

'He was such a gentle man, yet wonderfully brave. He was a curious mixture of being down-to-earth and practical, as well as sensitive, artistic and ingenious.'

'He sounds too perfect Mum, come on,' I dig.

'No, he wasn't perfect. He did appear even-tempered, but this masked a deep impatience with incompetence. "Why couldn't the fool use his sense of discretion," was his favourite saying. He had extraordinary intolerances and opinions as well. Some I really protested against, like, "All natives are lazy and dishonest".'

'Granny told me he wasn't at all religious.'

'That's right. He didn't have any faith, he went as far as to say he was an atheist. "I don't believe in any of that trash," he said. He had a deep intolerance of pomposity. Couldn't bear people putting on airs and pretences, or being gushy. But he was such a kind person. He would never have hurt anyone or lied. He was so funny too,' she goes on. 'He was such a good story-teller, a gift he inherited from his mother, Grace. I wish one of us had recorded some of his stories.'

As we walk on, I can sense Mum is still thinking about her father. 'After meals he rubbed his tummy,' she says doing the action, 'saying, "Oh Ducky, that was delicious." He loved chocolate eclairs and sausage rolls, and of course wines and

Gerald and Margaret, Kenya 1925

The Hon. A.E. Bingham and Mrs Bingham

Lunch, first day, 1926

Nanny and Anne beside their grass hut

Camp, second day!

Brick making

From left, Adam, George, James and Elardie, 1927

Women daggering hut

Margaret and Anne

Waterfall in flood, 1928

Gerald with his team of men

George, cooking in the kitchen

The back of M'Coben

Tobacco seed-beds

Tobacco picking

Elardie with chameleon

spirits. All the things which weren't good for his heart. But I should think his motto was that life was too short.'

Mum turns to me, a few tears in her eyes. 'I wish I had known him better. My father inspired great loyalty, as a serving officer at the age of twenty and then again in the Second World War. He inspired it in Margaret. He inspired it in me.'

CHAPTER FOURTEEN

I am sitting at Margaret's old desk reading her letters. Diana sits in the corner of the room, her face buried in a bird book. She is determined to discover the name of the large yellow bird we saw in a tree driving back from Bulawayo to M'Coben.

Fred pads into the room in his grey shorts, t-shirt and long socks. The outfit reminds me of a young boy's school uniform but somehow Fred gets away with it. He looks attractive. 'What are you reading?' he asks me, looking at an array of sheets scattered around me.

'Granny's, well, Margaret's letters. The ones she wrote to her mother.' I pick up a pile to show him.

'Do you have the letters Margaret's mother wrote back?'

'No, I wish I did.'

'I burnt them,' Granny had said during one of our sessions. 'I had so many you see, I didn't have space for them. The white ants would have probably eaten them anyway,' she shrugged.

As I continue to re-read the letters, I now desperately want to know if Granny's mother, Julian, expressed her fears of Margaret being in Africa. What did she say about the Trust business? Did she in any way try to persuade her to return to England? Did her letters give any signs that she thought Gerald wasn't good enough for her? While Margaret was waiting to hear back she continued to write home. She could not bear the thought of losing contact and wanted to share the everyday news with her mother. 'For my birthday treat we all went to the Matopos Hills for the day. It really is the most awe-inspiring place.' At this time she wanted her mother also to know just how much Gerald was doing, 'Gerald knows the tobacco process from start to finish, he will do the whole thing himself.' Yet within each letter there was something spitting back about the Trust business. She could not help mentioning it. It preyed on her mind, 'I have not gone quiet against the Trustees and their attitude. I think the conditions they tried to impose upon us outrageous.'

I would love to see the letter Margaret so anxiously waited for during those agonising six weeks. Julian was clearly worried about the primitiveness of the life her daughter had chosen to lead. An early letter, written by Granny on 18 July 1926, is a reassurance, of a sort.

'My darling Mother,

We could not help being amused by your idea of our position in the wilds, and of the uncivilised state of Rhodesia. As it happens, the Binghams live only four miles away and they are perfectly charming oldish people. We are just over forty miles from Bulawayo and the road is bad like all Rhodesian roads and it takes us two hours to get there. But once there, there are good doctors, dentists, shops and everything else we may want. There are other very nice neighbours all within a radius of five to fifteen miles, so once we are settled we shall not be in the least dull. The natives are extremely quiet, well-behaved men and we need never fear anything from one's own boys. The only danger might be in meeting travelling boys or drunk natives. I should never go off riding very far alone, but it would be perfectly all right for me to go and visit the Binghams as long as I take a dog and a good stick, the latter more for protection against snakes. We are bound to come across a good many snakes here as the place has never been inhabited before. Our boys killed a fourteen foot python by the river last week and Gerald and the foreman between them killed quite a big greenish snake near the lands – otherwise we are not troubled by any wild beasts. One might see an occasional leopard.'

'My mother was anxious for us,' Granny confided.

'Yes, I'm sure she was,' I had said after reading her this particular letter. 'Can you imagine what your parents must have thought about the "closeness" of the neighbours, the possibility of drunken natives, snakes and the odd leopard!'

'Oh,' she rocked with laughter. 'Yes, I hadn't thought of that. There were many things I didn't tell my mother though.'

'Like what?'

'We did encounter intruders but I didn't tell her until much later on. I remember one brilliant moonlit night, we had only been camping for a month.'

August 1926

Margaret sat up immediately, she could have sworn she had heard something outside. She looked across at Gerald who was sound asleep on his camp-bed. They had pushed two camp-beds together in their cramped quarters. She shivered, aware that only the canvas wall of the tent protected them from the outside. She hesitated whether to wake Gerald up. Perhaps she had imagined the noise? It sounded as if there was a dog outside. She brought her knees to her chest and hugged them tightly. She now heard solid footsteps in the grass, the noise was so close. She grabbed Gerald's arm. 'Wake up,' she said breathlessly. She opened the flap of the tent and froze when she saw a tall dark figure with a dog walking towards the tin shanty which they had made into a kitchen. She heard him roaming about amid the sounds of pots and pans.

'Someone's in our kitchen!' Margaret whispered loudly, exasperated that someone should dare to steal from under their nose. She watched Gerald forcefully pull on his boots and take the gun from under his pillow. 'You stay here,' he ordered. He moved slowly towards the kitchen. Margaret sat poised, waiting to hear a gun shot. Her heart was hammering. What if he's armed, if he's dangerous?

She let herself breathe again when she saw Gerald walk back into the tent. 'He must have cleared off,' Gerald guessed. 'He probably just wanted to steal some food, or money.'

Two evenings later, they had a plan. 'I will say goodnight to you and then pretend to go to sleep. I'll snore loudly,' Gerald whispered to Margaret. They were convinced that the intruder had returned the night before and now Gerald was determined to catch him.

'Fine,' she replied, 'but don't snore too quickly after saying goodnight, it won't sound realistic. Wait a few minutes and then start to snore.'

'Fine, good plan.' Gerald blew out the lantern and said goodnight.

'Goodnight, sleep well darling,' Margaret exaggerated loudly.

'Goodnight,' Gerald returned, louder still.

He sat on the edge of the bed with his gun at hand, and

they waited and waited. An hour passed and Gerald yawned, longing to lie down. He was about to do so, when they heard a sudden noise. He ran out and saw a figure. He held the gun up and fired two warning shots, one to the side of the man's head, and one just over.

Margaret flinched when she heard the sound. Thank goodness Gerald was such a good shot. What if he has hit the man? she thought, suddenly panicking as she heard the shots ring out loud in the still night air.

As the figure vanished once more into the darkness, Gerald hoped he had scared him enough not to come back. He walked back into the tent and laid the gun under his pillow. Instead of climbing into his own little camp-bed he walked over to Margaret's and lifted the cover over her. 'He's gone,' Gerald assured her. 'I don't think he'll be coming back.' With relief Margaret kissed him and Gerald squeezed into her small camp-bed. She did not feel frightened anymore. She felt safe with Gerald. As she lay awake, she told herself that she would not write and tell Mother about this incident, especially as her last letter had been so reassuring, saying there was nothing to fear except the occasional drunk native.

She finally drifted off to sleep, Gerald's arm still around her.

'The following year we were told by the local district police that our midnight visitor was convicted of murdering his wife with an axe and injuring another native. He suffered the death penalty,' Granny had explained. 'If he had come back again Gerald would have shot him. He was a well-known villain in the district and he died unmourned.'

'I should think so. To think he had been prowling around

your tent too.'

Even with the protection of Gerald, I shiver to think how vulnerable Margaret must have felt with her precious little girl surrounded by the unknown. Helen said that she felt terrified camping in Africa and refused to walk outside the tent at night. If she needed the loo she peed in a pot. There was no way she was going to risk encountering a leopard or a lion hungry for its next meal – apparently they mistook their little domed tents for rocks and had been known to sleep across them. It is no surprise that Granny felt infinitely safer once the house was built and she had proper solid walls around her. It is no wonder Margaret's family were worried too.

'I've done a piece!' Fred suddenly cries out, bringing me back to reality. Jigsaw pieces are scattered all over the table. He raises his arms in an expression of triumph. 'A piece a day and the Victoria Falls will soon be finished.'

'Well done,' Diana and I praise.

'Can you read me a letter?' Fred asks as he sits down next to me.

I pick up a random one and clear my throat.

'Our visitor, Captain Murphy, is still with us. He is not altogether an easy guest. I have never known anyone do so little. He sits about all day long and makes the sitting room in the most unholy muddle. He sits in each chair in turn and throws the cushions on to the floor when he feels hot, litters every table with tobacco and cigarette mess.'

I shift uneasily, a plume of smoke is rising from Diana's cigarette. With an amused smile she looks up from the bird book she is reading. Letters are scattered on the floor in front of me, hopelessly out of date order. Mum is having a 'siesta'.

I continue reading,

'He thinks he gets up early when he saunters into breakfast at 8.45am – I don't think he realises that Gerald is up and arranging all the farm duties for the day at 6am. He cannot bear the thought of discomfort, and looking at our photos of the early days here, he said, "I don't think I should be much use pioneering," with which I agreed silently!'

Fred laughs loudly. I am sure he thinks that Mum, Diana and I are the epitome of Captain Murphy. I show him a few old photographs of M'Coben when Margaret and Gerald were camping. He appears interested to see how it all began.

After Fred leaves I think about the question he asked me. Would I have been happy living like that? It is something I have asked myself a few times.

My first experience of camping was when I was about three. I remember going on the 'dreaded family holiday' to France. I don't think any of our family are natural campers. Dad could not put up the tents properly; Mum was over-tired and cross from having to do it all herself. Mum told me it rained constantly during that week. She also reminded me that I wet the lylo which I was sharing with Helen. However, the one thing I do remember vividly was the saucisson. I also had great fun sitting in the tent speaking make-believe French to anyone who was willing to listen.

I have never camped since. Now that I have RA I should think it's unlikely I'll ever have the opportunity again. 'You wouldn't be able to do it darling,' Granny told me frankly.

'I know. I don't think I mind too much either,' I had replied. 'Was Gerald happy living in a tent?'

'He was as happy as a sandboy,' she stated.

'And you?'

'I was as happy as a sandboy too.'

'Wasn't there anything you hated about living out in the wild with no roof over your head?' I pushed. To my mind I couldn't think of anything worse. I would miss my double-bed and a goose-down duvet too much.

'No, we were as happy as sandboys.'

I wished she would stop saying that. It was irritating me. What is a 'sandboy' anyway?

'Well, actually the lack of light was tiring.' At last, I thought, I am getting somewhere. 'It got dark at 7pm, winter or summer, and we had to use candles and lanterns. We went to bed very early, at around 9pm, because there wasn't much to do in the pitch black. The flying dust was also a terrible nuisance, it got into everything. That's why I cut my hair and nanny's. She had mousy blonde hair but I snipped it all off.' It reminded me of the time when Mum cut off my plaits so that my hair wouldn't get in my eyes playing tennis. She kept the long plaits in a drawer in the sitting room. She still has them.

'It was incredibly exciting working towards the house though,' Granny continued. 'I didn't mind the discomfort one bit. Think of the Africans who have always lived in huts. I rather relished it. Gerald and I loved the evenings. We were so hard at work during the day that we hardly saw one another. I always looked forward to eating our meal together around the fire,' she said, her face animated with the memory. 'The Africans brought eggs and chickens to the camp and Gerald shot guinea fowl, francolin, partridges and doves which were all prepared by the cook-boy. We were starving by supper time. It was a new life for me,' Granny stressed.

She was right. I began to see that there must be something extraordinarily liberating about living outside with a fire and under the stars. After living at Longford, it must have been a revelation for her to be with Gerald in the vast open outdoors of Africa at night. I am sure Gerald was relieved to get away from the stifled upper-class regime. What a relief not to have to get dressed for dinner and then wait for the gong before you were summoned to eat. Instead they could collapse around the fire after a long day, Margaret in a long loose summer dress, Gerald in his working trousers and shirt. I can see that they would have enjoyed the freedom of being their own masters. It must have given them a great sense of independence. They were also able to enjoy a rare closeness which came from building their home together. There must have been something very binding about working as a partnership to create their farm. Had Gerald stayed in England in the army or had a nine to five job, with Granny at home baking biscuits, their relationship might not have been so intimate.

'There were only a few moments when I longed for a proper bathroom or bed. But we were ever so happy,' Granny had said.

She made me realise how you can be happy without all the things you think you need. What is important is who you are with and what you are doing. Like Granny explained, they were building their future. The camping was, at times, tough but together they survived on very little and found the strength and courage from within themselves.

Suddenly, the image of Margaret and Gerald sitting around the fire eating roast partridge and living under the stars was incredibly romantic. I had realised, and not for the first time, that I was envious of Granny and the lifestyle she was able to choose. She and Gerald had health on their side, they were able to cope with living in rough conditions and be independent. It was exciting, wild, new and adventurous. It wasn't sitting at a desk, looking at a computer every day and popping out to the newsagents when you ran out of milk. They chose a different and challenging path. Rather than thinking 'I'm glad it wasn't me,' I found myself thinking, 'I wish it could have been me.'

CHAPTER FIFTEEN

August 1926

Margaret awoke to find her pillow coated in dust again. She looked like a Red Indian. For three days they had a makasa[1]. The flying dust was terrible, getting into everything. Margaret wrote her name in dust on the pillow. There is so much of it, she thought as she shook it out of her hair. As she looked down to the mattress she saw a small patch of blood. She vigorously pulled the sheet off the camp-bed and gathered it into a bundle. She sat back down again. She had been sure she was pregnant. The 'enemy' was late. What am I doing wrong? Are Gerald and I ever going to have another baby?' Anne is growing up quickly and needs friends to play with. I am beginning to think of this district as 'the barren valley'. There are so few children on any of the neighbouring farms. All Anne is saying at the moment is, 'Oh do hurry up you lazy boy.' Margaret knew she would cry if she dwelt on it any longer. Yet it was difficult not to be emotional when she felt so dirty after camping or 'pigging it' as she called it, for six weeks. Her mind quickly went to mail day. It was Thursday. English mail day. Today she would receive the letter from her mother in response to her railings over the Trustees, surely? These last six weeks had been hard. It was lucky she was kept so busy otherwise the wait would have been intolerable.

There was a small amount of water in the enamel basin and Margaret washed her face and hands. It would have been a joy to be pregnant while camping and not have to worry about the curse. She had started the enemy when she was

---

[1] Cold damp spell

twelve. When she had been at school or at home, she had simply put her large square linen sanitary towels into bags to be washed in the laundry room, and back they came, ironed and ready to use again. It was all done for you. It is these kind of things which I have taken for granted, she realised as she pulled on her dungarees. She still had the same towels she'd used at school which had loops at both ends and tape which pulled through to secure them to your waist. They lasted for years, at least that was something. Wouldn't it be an unimaginable irritant if I had to go into Bulawayo to buy the wretched towels every time?

Margaret heard noises outside. She drank the early morning tea George had made, and then went out to see what was going on. It was a beautiful still day. The 'makasa' was finally over.

She walked across the veldt, the ground was coarse and dry. As usual the boys were squabbling over who was going to collect the mail from the railway station at Nyamandhlovu. Gerald and Margaret realised that it was a wildly popular job because they liked to meet their friends from different neighbouring farms. As they waited for the train which brought parcels, meat and vegetables they congregated under the shade of a tree and had a party.

Margaret told them firmly that it was Adam's turn. And please return with the letter from home, she prayed again. The words she had written haunted her. 'I do not know what attitude you and Daddy are taking up and I cannot know for another six weeks, but if you, too, feel like the Trustees that Gerald cannot be trusted my bitter cup will indeed be full. And though it would break me in half to do it, I should never feel able to go home again...'

Margaret put it to the back of her mind. She must get on with the day ahead. There was so much to do. She found Gerald with the three native boys whom they had hired to find water. Water was the most pressing priority and they still had none. When they dug down, they had quickly struck very hard rock and had to resort to driving small bores with a hammer and chisel and setting daily explosions of dynamite to blast the rock. As the well deepened, the fuse wire was lengthened so as to allow the workers time to climb the rickety ladder up to the surface before the blast went off. The boys never went back down the hole until the next day as they feared one of the dynamite sticks had not ignited. As a result the whole procedure was taking longer than expected. They were becoming a familiar part of the scenery. All three came from a tribe who lived near the Zambezi. As Margaret watched them she couldn't help smiling at their strange appearances. Their bodies were tiny with large heads and heavily built shoulders. They wore tattered clothes, greasy hats and filed their teeth into sharp points rather like some sort of fish. Gerald caught her eye and walked over to her. 'Good morning,' he kissed her.

'Their hats are like gnomes' head-dresses,' Margaret whispered to him.

'They are not unlike gnomes themselves,' he whispered back.

Margaret watched them with fascination as they scrambled out of the hole and rushed madly away. 'Baas-op, baas-op'[1], the leader of the group shouted. Their hands were on their heads and their eyes were closed tightly shut waiting for the blast to go off. There were the occasional moments when

---

[1] Look out, look out!

Margaret thought, 'What am I doing here?' and this was one of them. Others included:

Trying to have a bath in a draughty tent

Squatting in the P.K.[1] on the rough loo seat

When she caught Anne washing her hair with 'dagga' – mud and water used for plastering the walls

When Gerald suggested making a pair of lizard shoes from a shot-by-mistake iguana

Eating lunch in the tin hut which heated up to a sweltering ninety-six degrees

Not having a telephone to call the doctor when Anne had a temperature of over a hundred and two degrees

When her kitchen was blown over by a whirlwind. The iron wall fell on her and all the scones in the oven were ruined.

At least there is never a dull moment, Margaret smiled as she went to find Anne and Nanny in the grass shelter. Anne had been staying in the hotel at Bulawayo until they could make her a brick hut but they missed her so much that Gerald had erected a grass shelter, just big enough for a camp-bed and Anne's pram. Keeping her at the hotel had also been too expensive. Anne had celebrated turning two on the ship coming over. She was growing up daily and talking fluently.

'Good morning Anne,' Margaret smiled.

'When is God going to jump down with my baby brother?' Anne asked in a disgruntled tone.

Margaret shrugged her shoulders and turned to Florence, the young English nanny. 'Did you sleep well?' Margaret thought Florence was very plain, 'the poor girl'. She wore such dreary dresses with dud brown lace-up shoes. Margaret thought she looked a little like Elsie England, the nursery maid

---

[1] 'Piccanin Kaia' meaning 'little house'

at Longford. Elsie didn't have quite such unfortunate goofy teeth though. However the main thing was Florence was devoted to Anne.

As Margaret took Anne to the kitchen to prepare some toast and porridge, she saw Elardie walking down the track on his way back from the Binghams. Gerald sent him out every morning with empty whisky bottles to fetch the milk. Margaret had made him a canvas bag with slots for the bottles, two on the front and two on the back, with a hole in the middle for his head. Elardie nodded politely at her. He did not speak a word of English, had never worked for a white man before, nor worn any proper clothes. When Margaret had first met him he had worn nothing but a loin cloth – a mere scrap of cloth covering his private parts! Most of the workers' clothes were scanty, some also only wearing loin cloths and old felt hats. Gerald and Margaret could not afford to dress the entire labour force but they decided that their house-boys, Elardie and George, must have a proper uniform. Margaret knew she would feel ill at ease cooking with George in the hot kitchen with him wearing next to nothing. 'It would be too awkward,' she had told Gerald. He agreed and the boys were given a pair of khaki shorts with a shirt and a white apron for George. Margaret didn't mention that she was also a little frightened of the strange intimacy of seeing the boys naked, especially when Gerald was out on the lands rather than working close to the house site.

The kitchen was small and square and made out of corrugated iron. It was just big enough for a table and a wood burning Doverstove. George and Elardie peered at Anne and she pulled a horrified face. 'The black men are coming after me!' she started to cry. Margaret tried not to laugh as she apologised. This wasn't the first time. Anne was deeply puzzled by the colour of the workers' skin. On one occasion she had screamed in front of the water men, 'No like these kaka men!'

After breakfast Margaret stayed around the house-site. She was taken up with paying the native women for the thatching grass. Gerald had designed a simple three-roomed cottage – two bedrooms and a sitting room. They had decided to have a thatch roof and Margaret had put out a plea for thatching grass. Margaret was aware that women were not allowed to work in their house, it made the husbands jealous. They believed that the women's place was at home, looking after the children or working in the fields. The women, however, were keen to help and have some extra money.

Margaret sat with Anne watching the women walk towards the house-site with great bundles of the cut grass on their heads and babies strapped to their backs. Margaret had never seen such a magical sight. An old woman was approaching, she had no hair and was wearing a long navy printed dress which had been made at the local native store, the pattern dating back to the early missionaries. Behind her was George's wife, wearing a torn cotton skirt with an equally tattered shirt and a white kerchief in her hair. The child skipping behind her wore nothing. Margaret handed George's wife a well-earned threepence for her bundle of thatching grass which was placed on a platform of veldt timber. George's wife smiled radiantly when handed the pennies. She looked young, probably only sixteen, and Margaret thought how beautiful she was with her clear skin and dark eyes.

Margaret spent the rest of the morning making curtains

and straw mattresses to keep them warm at night in their future home. It was now mid-day when the farm labour broke off for two hours and Margaret was about to have a bath. She tended to have a wash in the middle of the day when it was warmer and the sun shone into the tent. Elardie and Adam heated the water in five-gallon drums over the open fire. Margaret stood in the shallow canvas camping bath and quickly scrubbed the dirt off her. Because of such a limited supply of water she felt permanently grubby. It would be wonderful finally to have a proper enamel bath, she thought. I don't know why Mother had a hip bath in her bedroom when their bathroom was so large and one of the only few in the house. In fact, there were forty-seven rooms at Longford so just one bathroom was extraordinary. Oh Mother, what are you going to think of my letter? Will you be angry? She scolded herself to stop thinking about it. 'I tell you who I'm angry with,' she muttered under her breath as she dried herself, 'that Campbell is a disaster.' Campbell, the builder, had turned up late and drunk again and Gerald had furiously sent him home. He had organised a brick-making gang but the first lot of 'slop' bricks, made near the spruit from a mixture of mud and sand, had been a complete failure. They had come out of the kiln a good colour but when dropped on the ground they crumbled like pastry.

'The silly idiot of a brick maker has been using the wrong soil,' Gerald had said. 'Why couldn't Campbell use his sense of discretion?' At the time, Margaret didn't like to tell him it was probably their fault and that they were bound to make mistakes to begin with. 'Silly idiot,' she had said back. She now realised that Campbell was indeed a total fool and that after this work was done they must never use him again. Gerald decided to try the valley soil near the river for the next lot of bricks and ordered the gang of workers to get going at once. The brick boy, clad in an old sack, was permanently in a hole in the ground near the river busily filling the 'forms' with mixed wet soil to make three bricks at a time. The forms were taken away by the rest of the brick gang and set out on the ground in a neat row, covered with cut grass before they went into the kiln for firing.

Gerald prayed that these bricks would be better than the first batch as they needed them urgently for the house and the two tobacco-curing barns. However, the crumbled ones from the first batch would be used to line the tobacco seed beds and the best of the well-burnt ones could be used for the cottage. At least building had started.

After George's vegetable soup for lunch, Margaret settled down in the tent for an hour. Her neck was aching and she stretched out her shoulders. She barely saw Gerald during the day so always looked forward to the evenings when they could sit, eat and talk around a blazing fire.

Gerald spent most of the day with the workers, gradually clearing and stumping the bush before ploughing the land. They were going to grow maize and tobacco. Gerald was most often found crawling along on his hands and knees preparing the tobacco seed-beds. But if he wasn't doing that he was busy making the tracks accessible so that the wagon and farm implements would work. Gerald had quickly set high standards and he expected the same of others too. Any worker who did not pull his weight would be given a severe ticking off. He had already caught one of the boss-boys staggering around drunk, with a cut on his forehead. Furious, Gerald told him to soak the wound with disinfectant and go to bed immediately.

So far, the labour force appeared to be working hard but Margaret was frustrated to notice that they would become slack as soon as Gerald turned his back. Some would even nod off under the shade of a tree, thinking no one could see them. When Gerald returned, they set to again as if they'd never stopped. There was so much to do that she had had strong words with them, 'Back to work! We don't pay you to do nothing,' but it seemed to be in vain. She realised that it was Gerald whom they saw as the leader. He was the one who paid them.

Mr Mitchell, one of their neighbours, warned Gerald never to pay the workers in notes because they hid the money in the thatch of the roofs only to find the white ants ate them. Not surprisingly Margaret had learnt that the Africans had a deep mistrust of the value of notes. Gerald had provided them with old tobacco tins in which to keep their coins.

She took her writing paper and pen out of the suitcase. 'Anne now weighs twenty-nine pounds and her little legs are as straight and firm as one could wish for and she has at last got a lovely colour.' She knew Mother liked to hear news of Anne. She went on to describe how the natives had begun from almost the first day to flock to their camp asking for employment. In no time at all their labour force was growing in numbers. She now had three house-boys, George, Elardie and a newcomer called Adam. James, the head farm boy, a delicate man who had had tuberculosis had an army of twenty other workers. George had been one of the first to build his own kraal at the foot of the kopje and bring his wife and children.

'How many wives do you have?' Gerald had asked him. Gerald could not bear the thought of him bringing an army of wives and children with him.

'Only one,' he replied holding up one finger.

Margaret found the concept of 'buying a wife' extraordinary. Thankfully many of their workers could not afford many wives. Wives cost about £10 or the equivalent in cattle, anything from five to ten head. However, most of them did have a family, it was only Elardie and the four other piccanins who were on their own. 'Such a workforce may seem extravagant, but it costs us just under a pound a month. I think we shall live all in for about twenty pounds a month – including wages, washing and everything so you see house bills are cheap compared to England. And there are no rates or taxes out here!' Each worker was assigned to different tasks, she explained. One of the more skilled and better paid jobs was training the oxen and these boys were called the 'boss-boys'. Margaret was intrigued by the sounds of the boys cracking the long ox-hide whip while shouting special instructions to the animals.

Two boys were busy constructing a farm road from their site, which would join the main road making the journey to Nyamandhlovu station five miles shorter. 'This is vital as we have to go to Nyamandhlovu frequently. When the bulky orders like flour, sugar and maize-meal come out by train to Nyamandhlovu station, the ox-wagon, drawn by a span of fourteen oxen, sets off in the early morning in order to cover the seventeen miles, returning by nightfall. The plans for the house are moving at a desperate pace.' Campbell appeared to think that four days was a full working week. He always left early on a Friday to prepare himself for a boozy weekend ahead and returned to the farm on Tuesday, unable to make sense because he was still tight. 'It is like squeezing a dry lemon to get this Campbell to work and every day brings us nearer to the rains,' Margaret wrote, feeling better just for venting her frustrations. 'But the farm looks like a hive of bees with all the activity! Gerald is working terribly hard. I'm not worrying too much about the garden at the moment. I am only concentrating on the vegetables. I have planted tomatoes, beans, peas, radishes, sage and thyme, lettuce, beetroot and parsley. They are beginning to show but it's taking time because we are so short of water. We use any left-over bath and washing-up water.'

Margaret put the pen down for a moment. Her head felt like a heavy brick. Each worrying thought was clinging to her like a magnet, she could not drive them away. She closed her eyes. Think of something else, she said as she rested her head against the pillow. She wondered what she would be doing if she were in London. Probably going to the theatre and visiting friends. She would be at a dinner party with Mary or at a dance in her blue silk dress, velvet cloak and kid gloves. She would be brushing her long hair and clipping it into a bun. Maybe she and Gerald would be at Longford. If it was hot they would be at the Old Garden, bathing in the river. She might be riding. Or walking around the garden with Mother. The roses would be wonderful at this time of year. Why haven't I heard anything from you Mother? No cable. Nothing. I am sorry if I accused you wrongly for mistrusting Gerald. I must know what you are thinking. If I have no letter today I shall go mad. She put a hand through her hair. It was grimy with dust because she had not washed it for weeks. She found a pair of scissors in the suitcase and ruthlessly cut through a greasy chunk, watching it drop to the floor. Nanny's hair will have to be cut too, she thought. Margaret swore she would never grow it long again, and more importantly, as she hacked off the rest, she promised not to hanker after the past.

She finished her letter and went to the kitchen to find George. Every afternoon she set about teaching herself and George how to cook. She had bought a very good recipe book from the cooking course at High Street Kensington. It had meat and vegetable dishes, and pictures of puddings. So far they had made cakes and pastries, she had failed to put butter in one of her cakes but that didn't matter. Perhaps she would start a new style of cake. They had also burnt the top of the apple pie. 'I have burnt apple-egg and I burnt top of pie too,' George said. He looked so distressed Margaret thought he might burst into tears. Margaret was learning how to prepare meat dishes. She had also taught George to make butter with the hand churn, something she had learnt to do at the dairy at Longford. Margaret yearned for a fridge as, despite George's best efforts, the butter was always soft and greasy. However, George was quite a find. He had worked for a European before and his English wasn't too bad. Margaret had asked him if he would teach her Zdebele[1], and in return she would teach him to speak better English. He had nodded with enthusiasm. Margaret wished Gerald would try and learn the language too but he showed little interest, preferring to wave his hands around and perform actions as instructions.

George knew how to make bread and had learnt to produce

---

[1] Dialect spoken by the Matabele tribe

yeast too. He is teaching me a thing or two, she thought, as she watched him soak the dried hops with a little flour, sugar and salt. Margaret didn't like the strong smell of the yeast, it smelt like beer. George poured the liquid into a bottle and when the inkosikazi[1] wasn't looking he quickly took a gulp before carefully tying the cork with a piece of string. 'Don't think I didn't notice that,' Margaret smiled to herself.

Margaret remembered loving going with Mother down to the kitchen to plan the menus with the head cook. As a treat they were always given a piece of chocolate at the end of the visit.

The kitchen at Longford was a large lofty room, lit by windows round the top part of the walls. She felt twinges of envy remembering the polished copper pots of every shape and size, jelly moulds and mixing bowls, the large kitchen table down the centre of the room and the two wall ovens. The warm open fire at the end of the room had a hand operated spit in front of it. Gerald would build her a lovely kitchen soon, she told herself. Be patient!

They would not be in this tin shanty forever.

She flicked through the recipe book. Now she was like her mother, planning the menus. She was going to cook a stew for the evening. The meat was stored in the home-made meat-safe housed in the round dairy hut behind the house-site, where they also kept the milk separator. Gerald had made a four-foot-square metal box, divided into two shelves for the meat and any leftovers, and covered with netting to prevent flies getting in. A tank on top of the shelves was filled with cold water every day. This tank had small holes around the edge and the water seeped slowly through into a small trough

---

[1] Queen

144

underneath. Pieces of cloth, attached by hooks, were submerged into the trough water and hung around the safe to keep the contents cool. Milk, cream and butter also stood in bowls of water with a cloth over the top, the evaporation keeping it fairly cold. Keeping food fresh and cool was a daily struggle. The heat in the kitchen itself was so terrific that each dish was flavoured with the sweat from her brow!

It was seven o'clock. Margaret had helped Florence give Anne her nightly bath. As usual they had washed and dried her as quickly as possible, wrapped her in a blanket and put her straight into her pram-bed with a hot-water bottle against the sudden cold.

There was nothing more stunning than the sun setting, Margaret thought, with the vivid red and orange skies throwing the wooded hillside into a dark purple silhouette. Then, like a black curtain, darkness fell quickly.

Gerald was helping himself to a large sun-downer of whisky. 'Sit down darling. Keep still. Adam will be back soon.' He walked over to her and touched her shoulders. 'They are rigid,' he told her. Margaret breathed deeply, circling her neck and shoulders.

Minutes later, Margaret saw Adam walking slowly along the track, laden with a bag of vegetables in one hand, a box of eggs in the other, bacon and butter balancing on his head, a parcel of meat under his arm and their mailbag over his shoulder. Although she had seen this sight many times before she still was astonished at how much he could carry.

Her heart was beating fast as he handed her the mailbag with BARRY stamped on it. The heavy bag smelt strongly of canvas. It was an exciting smell. Before opening any letters she had to half-cook the fresh meat straight away and soak the vegetables in water. Margaret unpacked the large slabs of grey meat which smelt like dried blood. She tried not to breathe in too much and brushed the flies away. It was important to cook it partially immediately otherwise it would go off. She handed the meat to George who placed it on the stove.

When the meat was cooking Margaret finally sat down on her own and unlocked the padlock. The weekly edition of the *Bulawayo Chronicle* lay on top, their only source of world and local news. She discarded it quickly along with two more envelopes. Then she saw the letter with her mother's familiar handwriting.

CHAPTER SIXTEEN

Mum, Diana and I are in the sitting room. I have just read them the letter Margaret wrote in reply to her mother's letter after the Trust business. Again, I wish I could see the letters sent from England.

'It's strange to think that it was our mother who wrote that,' Mum begins. 'When I read the letters I think of her as Margaret.'

Diana agrees. 'Although she signs herself, "little girl", what she says seems so much older than she actually was. When you think she was still only twenty-three.'

'Granny says she grew up quickly going to Africa,' I tell them. 'I remember her saying to me, "I led a sheltered life before I was married, but the moment we went to Africa I grew up overnight. I had to."'

'Well, she was learning to be a mother, adapting to a completely new lifestyle. Then the business with the Trust was miserable,' Mum says almost to herself. 'Read the letter again Alice, will you?'

I pick it up and start reading.

'My darling Mother,

You really can have no idea what a wonderful relief your letters were backing up our buy and so interested by our enterprise. I am very sorry I ever wrote as I did, but it was such a bitter blow at the time, and we were both so anxious and worried. Please forgive me all that I said, I see now it was wrong of me and Daddy has just shown us what really good backing we have got at home, by lending us the money with not so much as one word of quibble or question. We realise now that the person who is really to blame and who has let us down worst is our double-faced lawyer Maynard. Please forgive me, your very loving little girl, Margaret.'

'The Trust money was finally cabled to them a year later,' I say. 'It was not the full sum, but £4,000. It probably did not seem like a great triumph because the money should have been given freely. Still, at least it came and Granny was able to pay her father back.'

Mum sits forward and turns to me. 'Do you remember me telling you that before I married your father I went to Peshawar? I was working for the War Office attached to the High Commission. I was twenty-two and pretty immature. It's in Pakistan, Alice,' Mum says as she watches me trying to work it out for myself. 'It was a great adventure for me just as it would have been for Granny going to Africa. Head Office told us to take out two years' supply of tampax, toothpaste, loo rolls and so on.'

'What was it like?' Diana smiles.

'My initial reaction was one of horror. The people in our little outpost were so peculiar, unlike any of our friends or family. The heat, the dust and the smells were also hard to get used to. To make things worse I was working for a really dour man called Richard. He looked as if he had a permanent bad smell under his nose and he made my life miserable.'

'Oh Pam,' Diana says sympathetically.

'He constantly undermined my position as senior secretary, and then he demoted me which meant a big drop in my salary.

He had a thin stringy wife too.'

'What a bugger.' Diana lights a fag.

'I was so homesick. I wrote to Mum telling her that I didn't want to stay. I was tempted to pack up my bags and leave.'

'What did Granny say?' I ask.

'She wrote back a firm letter saying I must stay. I could just hear her saying, "You stick it out Pamela, don't let the wretched man win." She told me that I would always feel a failure if I returned. I think I knew in my heart that it would have been feeble to give in,' Mum confesses. 'It would have been much easier to tell me to come home, I know she missed me but that wasn't her style.'

'It must have got better because you did stay,' Diana suggests.

'Yes. "Richard the Terrible" was succeeded by "Norman the Great" and we got on well from the start. My first job in the morning was to cellotape his sock on to his wooden leg. He lost his leg during the war. He reinstated my position and my salary and he became a close friend. Life became one big round of parties and play. I learnt to play polo and swear like the men, I played golf, and had lessons flying a two-seater plane.'

'I didn't know you could fly,' I say.

'I was good at taking off but could never find my way back to the little airport. I travelled a great deal with Klaus too.'

'Oh yes, the German boyfriend who you nearly married,' I mention. Mum did once tell Helen and me about him. We occasionally wonder what life would have been like being German. Well, we wouldn't be around at all.

'I had a wonderful time and I think it did do me a lot of

good. It broadened my outlook on life. The only trouble was that when I returned to England everything seemed drab and boring and nobody was in the slightest bit interested in hearing about Peshawar. I hated it. So, I chucked in my job and went off to America. I had grown up a lot in those two years. I was a different person.'

'What did you do in America?' I ask, surprised by how adventurous Mum was. It's easy not to realise that your mother had a 'life' before you came along.

'I worked for a brides magazine,' she laughs. 'I worked for a silly woman who tottered around in high heels with jangling bracelets. It was dull. America was wonderful though, and a great place for young people. I must take you to New York sometime Alice. I know you'd love it.'

Mum and Diana have gone for an evening walk. I'm sitting under the thatched shelter drinking a special African orange drink with vodka. Fred made it for me and it's addictive. I should be productive and write some postcards home but I don't feel in the mood. It was something Mum said which has made me think, 'What if?'

People ask me now, 'How did you come to terms with your RA?'

I tell them that I haven't and never will. Why should I accept having RA? There is nothing redeeming about the illness.

'Don't you think the RA has made you a better person?'

Being ill has changed me but I certainly do not think I am a better person. It has taught me not to take things or friends for granted but perhaps that is something I should have known anyway.

'But maybe it was "meant to be" because you have found your writing?' they persevere, desperately trying to persuade me to see the good that has come out of it. I am lucky to have found something I passionately enjoy doing. Writing means so much to me and I would now feel lost without it. But I don't believe that it is 'meant to be'. What could I have achieved if I had always been well? Each different path has new adventures. If I had led a full active life I might have found something equally fulfilling.

What would have happened if I had travelled to the States? I was eighteen when I won a tennis scholarship to America. Days before signing the contract I was diagnosed with RA. 'What if I had never got RA?' I occasionally ask Mum. The question tends to crop up when I'm feeling vulnerable and unwell. 'You might still be in the States,' she guesses, 'Or you might have married an American. Or you might be working in a PR firm in London. Actually you would be hopeless working in an office, you have enough trouble finding your car keys.'

'You might be working for the sewage company,' Dad chips in. 'It's no use wondering,' he tells me, 'It's a pointless game.'

Yet sometimes I can't help myself wondering.

When Mum said she would take me to New York she meant it so well. I would enjoy going and I would love to go with Mum. But I'd also like to go on my own just as she did. It made me feel envious that Mum and Granny were able to travel. My continuing reliance on my mother does not allow me to feel independent or 'grown up'. Being 'taken' somewhere makes me feel more like a child always in need of an escort.

I take another sip of my vodka. This is the reality, I think to myself. For the past six years I haven't had a chance to travel. I am grateful that I am here and that I have the devoted support of my mother and aunt. I'm hoping that it will be possible to make a new life for myself when I return too. I mustn't lose sight of that. My parents realise too that I need a life away from them. I expect they need a life away from me, too.

I decide that the point about the 'what if?' question is that even though I think about it, it doesn't haunt me any more. I do think about my tennis, I do look back to the past, but I am no longer obsessed by it. Life does move on.

When I get back home I will start making plans to live in London.

CHAPTER SEVENTEEN

Diana and I are swimming in Fred and Betty's pool. It's more like a hole in the ground half full with sludgy green water. The floor is disgustingly greasy and full of pods which I keep thinking are snakes. It starts to rain heavily. Diana tells me that whenever I walk outside the heavens seem to open. She tells me I must be cursed. It's not easy getting out of the pool in a hurry. I have to get up the slimy steps on my bottom, Diana stands behind me just in case I slip. Diana is great because she doesn't fuss over me. In fact she is laughing at me as I finally stand straight. I can't look particularly elegant and unfortunately my skin hasn't changed colour. I'm still the colour of plain flour. Paul, the gardener, says hello while we shiver in our costumes. He has a look on his face which says we are mad to be swimming in the rain.

I pick up my towel, dismayed to find hundreds of ants crawling over it. 'You should have put it on the chair silly girl,' Diana says, 'here, have mine.'

We sit under the shelter of the verandah, drying off. 'I asked Granny if she could remember any real high points living in Africa,' I tell Diana as she lights a cigarette.

'Oh yes?' She looks up. 'What did she say?'

'She came up with just one thing!'

I watch Diana as she is thinking hard. I shake my head. 'You won't be able to guess. First of all she said,' – I imitate Granny's punchy voice,

'"I don't know."

"You can't think of one?" I asked incredulously.

And then in an equally curt tone, "I'll think about it."

"What were the low-points?"

She then began to reel off a rhythmical list. "One of the most frightening times was when we were still camping in the tents. It was a race against time to get our house built before the rains. During that anxious time we also had our first experience of fighting a veldt fire. The worries of the house were put into perspective when I believed I had lost Gerald."'

October 1926

Margaret sat on a tin crate brushing Anne's dark hair. She was surrounded by their luggage which had been collected from Nyamandhlovu. Wooden cases and boxes were piled up against the mimosa trees and raised off the ground by stones to prevent white ants wrecking the contents. White ants were larger than black ants and were a menace, eating wood, paper, fabric with an insatiable appetite. The luggage was stacked up high and had to be repeatedly moved and turned over to get rid of them. Yet already there were the tell-tale mud-covered tracks of the white ants up the side of the boxes.

Margaret was busy from dawn to dusk, making mosquito netting, window frames using wood hacked off their luggage cases or sewing curtains and bedcovers for Anne and themselves. If only they had the house. The brickwork on the house was finished, the roof timbers were up and the thatching grass was being cleaned and combed with a large primitive wooden tool to get rid of surplus seed.

Margaret longed to get her family under a proper roof. The merciless gales were making life in the tent unbearable. The heat seemed to be brewing up while the veldt was parched, the standing grass almost white, all the sap taken out of it till it was as brittle as straw. It was difficult to find anywhere to sit and be cool. The repressive heat left Gerald and Margaret anxious, continually scanning the heavy skies in fear that a storm would break.

Margaret went to find Anne. She wanted to take her for a walk and look at the plot which was going to be the kitchen garden.

Elardie jumped up and screamed in terror. 'Umlilo! Umlilo!'[1] he said repeatedly pointing to the farm next door at Mpandeni, opposite the Binghams.

Gerald looked over, 'Good boy, quick, fika!'[2] Gerald grabbed two of the boys and Elardie sprinted after him.

'What's wrong?' Margaret panicked as she approached them.

'Fire. Hambro's farm.'

'Oh lord.' She swallowed hard.

'You stay here, we can manage. I'll take the boys, don't worry.'

Margaret nodded. 'Be careful,' she called out to their retreating backs.

It was now 1pm. Gerald and the boys had been gone for a good hour. Margaret ran to the car and put some sacks on the backseat. 'Quick, in, help!' George and Adam jumped into the car along with James, the head farm boy. I can't sit and do nothing, she thought as she drove as fast as she could down the dirt track. Gerald cannot cope on his own. What if he gets hurt? A sick feeling hit her stomach. Anne and Nanny are safe in their hut, they can't be touched because the spruit mercifully

---

[1] Fire [2] Quick

divides them from the fire. But what if Gerald is injured?

Margaret mustered any boy she passed on the way, but it wasn't enough. What had been a few flickering flames had now turned into an uncontrollable fire.

The boys were scared. All Margaret could think about was Gerald. As they drew nearer she could see that the flames, fanned by the wild gusts of wind, were now travelling at a frightening pace towards their farm.

'Gerald! Gerald,' she shouted in vain. She should have come sooner.

She took a sack and set to work with the boys, beating down the fire. She seized anything she could lay her hands on. The boys were attacking the fire with bundles of sticks. Bushes were torn apart and slashed against the flames. 'Gerald!' she screamed again, as her arms pounded down against the flames with all the strength she had in her.

She looked over desperately to Elardie and George and saw them making a fire against a fire to prevent the flames spreading and travelling towards M'Coben. She looked up, the fire was rushing towards them at alarming speed and Margaret ran away from it, her legs shaking and sore. Small and large buck were leaping around her, fright in their eyes. Margaret screamed as a long brown snake shot past her, its head and front end reared high above the ground. There were insects everywhere, lizards and geckos all fleeing from the fire. Spring hares and civet cats, even tortoises struggling to hurry out of the path of flames.

This is a hopeless task, she realised in despair, tears streaming down her face. I don't care about losing our precious grasslands, that's not important, but dear God, she prayed, let Gerald be safe. 'Gerald,' she cried again.

It was now 4.30pm. Margaret had not seen any sign of Gerald. She bent over in exhaustion, holding her stomach. Her throat felt like parchment, her face like a rough nutmeg grater. Dirt and sweat lined her forehead. Nothing was left except black earth, innumerable little spirals of smoke and an eerie silence. She tried to lift up her arms but they were so weak that she could hardly feel them anymore.

'Margaret.' She heard a faint voice, 'Margaret.' The voice was travelling towards her.

'Gerald, is that you, Gerald!' She ran in the direction of his voice, feeling some kind of strength returning. She could not see anyone. 'Gerald.' As she saw his slim figure striding across the black charcoal earth her heart burst with relief and joy. They flung their arms around each other and Margaret sobbed into his shoulder. 'It's all right,' he whispered gently.

Relieved grins spread across the workers' faces as they made their way back to the farm. Gerald and Margaret held hands tightly. No more words needed to be said as they returned home.

Two thousand acres were burnt along with a stretch of thatching grass.

'I'm sure it does the grass good to be burnt,' Margaret suggested positively as they helped themselves to an extra large sundowner. Margaret drank Cape Brandy. Gerald was relieved to see that she wasn't too upset. He had explained to her that they were only thirty bundles of thatching grass behind. It wouldn't set them back much.

'No real harm was done, was it?' Margaret continued.

He admired the way she was able to see something good come out of every bad situation. 'No,' he agreed, gazing out at the mimosa tree. No real harm was done. The most important thing was that they were both safe. It just meant one step backwards. Heaven only knows when they would finally be in their house. They had lost grass which meant lost time. If a tropical thunderstorm broke over them now, they would be, as the Binghams from next door had so eloquently told him, 'surely washed away'.

'No real harm was done,' he repeated, 'everything will be fine.'

'My father felt very responsible for Mum. I am sure that there were moments when he wondered what he was doing bringing her out into the wilds of Africa,' Diana says after I tell her the fire story. 'If something had happened to her he would never have forgiven himself. Those early days were extremely tough. But a high point must have been when she woke up in the house for the first time?' Diana suggests. 'Surely?'

'Well yes, I know it was, Granny described it vividly. She even remembered the date. She said that they felt like they were in a palace.'

Margaret woke up feeling as if she was in the Ritz Hotel. She lay back on the bed and sighed with happiness. 31 October 1926, she thought to herself. I shall remember this morning until the day I die.

Life couldn't be more exciting. Gerald was going to make the petrol boxes and packing cases into cupboards, dressing tables, washstands and bedside tables. Once she had covered the furniture with pretty fabrics and put the curtains up they would be so smart. Well, at any rate they would feel like kings and that was all that mattered. She was going to write to Mother and tell her how happy they were.

Gerald stirred and kissed her good morning. For a moment he forgot where he was, expecting to see the inside of the tent and a pillow of dust. Instead he looked up to the thatch and a feeling of luxury swept over him. All their hard work had come good in the end and they had not had one single drop of rain to contend with. They had been lucky after all.

'Muhle, muhle,'[1] George and Elardie chanted as each case was opened and Margaret showed them the things for the house – beds, chairs, china, pictures, cutlery, a dessert service. Margaret was delighted to see all their wedding presents again. 'Muhle,' the boys repeated as they looked at a pair of silver candlesticks and a silver sugar basin. Gerald and Margaret laughed.

'Did they think we would always sleep on camp beds in tents and live higgledy-piggledy?' Margaret giggled as she nudged Gerald.

The rain has stopped and Diana and I go for a short walk. I am feeling well and my ankle finally feels normal since the operation. I am constantly wearing the multi-coloured splint. As we walk on slowly, Diana points out various flowers, shrubs and trees but I am hopeless at remembering names. There's an enormous banana tree at the back of the house and an avocado tree but the fruit is not ripe yet.

'It's changed a lot since we were here,' Diana explains. We walk into the old kitchen and store room, both now neglected.

---

[1] Grand – very good

They are more of a dumping ground. Beyond the house, in all directions, are work rooms, garages, lean-tos for trucks, the diesel tanks. The old windmill is there, although no longer operative. Granny and Gerald had bought a second hand windmill from their neighbours, the Mitchells, who lived at 'Spring Grange'. I can remember having ridiculous conversations with Granny about how a windmill worked. It's one of those things you know you learnt at school and ought to know. In the end I understood that the windmill pumped water into a large corrugated iron tank built up on a mound of stone and soil five feet above ground level so that the water could run downhill to the house.

'The well has been filled in,' Diana says.

'This was where they found water?' I tend to feel emotional when I stand on a spot where I know the ghost of a story lies. They found water just as they moved into the house. Now, finding water was a high point.

October 1926

The return journey from Bulawayo always caught Margaret out. The rough roads were tiring and she was exhausted. Her head ached, every bump, spruit and donga seemed to shake her bones. When she saw the welcoming face of George she felt relieved, anticipating the evening meal ahead. She was hungry.

'What are the boys doing?' Gerald muttered as he parked the car under the mimosa tree. The Zambezi boys with their filed teeth and greasy hats were jumping up and down in a frenzied state. Gerald jumped out of the car and rushed over to the boys who showed him a sample of sand which was damp. They had come to the end of hard rock and had started digging through sandstone. Margaret, Florence and Anne joined them and from Gerald's elated expression she knew what was to come.

'We've found water!' Gerald shouted.

Florence smiled radiantly, forgetting about the gaping black holes in her mouth. She had just been to the dentist in Bulawayo and had four of her front teeth pulled out. Margaret and Gerald hugged each other with joy. Gerald took her into his arms and they danced.

'We've found water at last!' he cheered as he twisted her around. Elardie and George joined them, along with some of the farm workers. They clapped and chanted. Finding water after three months of hard slog was something worth celebrating.

After an evening bath Margaret sat down with some paper and a pen, Anne curled beside her. 'Dear mother, well it really has been a red-letter week, water is there!'

'There were many high points. Granny only came up with one, but she knew there were many. It's sometimes hard when you're put on the spot. Your mind goes blank,' I say as we walk outside the security gate. Diana is going to take me to the old waterfall where they used to play.

'What did Granny come up with then? You said she gave you one example. It must have been having me?' she suggests.

'No, afraid not. After thinking about it for at least twenty minutes she called out to me in an excited tone, "Alice, I remember a high point, darling where are you?" I was in the kitchen. I had in fact forgotten I had asked her the question in the first place. She said,' and I breathe in and wrinkle my nose before I say,

'"I dined at Government House, Bulawayo and I sat next to King George VI. He had a little stutter but we talked non-stop. I actually had to tell him to talk to the lady on his other side. Sir, you must talk to Mrs Tredgold, I said to him. The princesses were there and Gerald sat next to the Queen."'

CHAPTER EIGHTEEN

Fred feeds Hairy Mary a steroid pill wrapped in a large globule of greasy butter.

Hairy Mary has arthritis. Her back legs slip when she tries to get up, she can't really walk properly. Fred dips his chubby fingers into the soft butter again and this time Katie eagerly licks the butter off his hand.

Fred then swallows his own muti[1] which Betty puts in a little dish by his breakfast every morning. Fred takes steroids too. Between us and the dogs our steroid intake is pretty high.

'I've got to see to Paul's hand after breakfast,' Betty tells us as she clears the plates. 'He cut it on one of the gardening forks.'

'Do you look after your workers?' I ask her.

'Yes, if it's something simple. It helps having been a nurse. Anyone who's seriously ill goes to the hospital. I expect your grandmother helped the families?'

'Yes, she did. It was a large part of her life,' I say, thinking back to one of our conversations.

'I was taken up with my medical sessions every morning. Right from the beginning, even when we were camping, native women came to me to ask for muti for their babies.'

'Did you realise that you would have to help them or was it totally unexpected?'

'I hadn't thought about it at all. I had to immediately go off to Bulawayo to buy the basic medicines. I bought bicarbonate of soda, dressings for wounds and burns, iodine,

---

[1] Medicine

aspirin, quinine, Epsom salts, cotton wool in large rolls and castor oil. I always saved old laundered linen for bandages. I kept it all in a box underneath my bed until we could afford to build a store-room.'

Granny described how she had learnt that the people had a real terror of going into hospital. By the time a very sick person had reached the nearest hospital their condition was often fatal, or their wound so infected that it was beyond medical aid. To them, a hospital was a place where you either died or had an arm or leg amputated.

'It was quite a responsibility on my own,' she explained seriously. 'I realised that until more hospitals and clinics were built locally for the families, the fear of going to one would never be cured. The nearest hospitals and doctors were in Bulawayo. We badly needed a hospital in Nyamandhlovu.'

'Describe a typical session to me,' I asked, unable to imagine it myself.

'The women and children with babies strapped on to their backs came in a crowd at around ten o'clock. They were seen one after another. I made it a firm rule that I would not treat any patient until they had washed their hands in the basin provided. The most common complaint was malaria. I gave them aspirin at first to bring down the temperature, and then quinine the following day. You could see their black skin turning grey. They felt ghastly. I also had to bandage feet which I didn't enjoy. The young children often stubbed their toes badly as they never wore shoes.'

'Did anyone have rheumatoid arthritis? What would you have given me?'

'I remember a lame old man had arthritis, he couldn't do

much around the farm. I gave him Epsom salts.'

'I've tried them. I had to bathe in them and then immediately get out of the bath and into bed.'

'Yes, that's right. Did the salts help you, darling?'

'No, not really. Did any of them see witch doctors?'

'Yes, the head boy's wife, a terrible old shrew, went off to see one. Some weeks later she returned amidst jubilation and celebration with the story of how the witch doctor had pulled a snake from inside her. Probably a tape worm, I should think.'

'How absurd. I do, oddly enough, believe in their powers, but he must have planted the snake inside her. What was the worst thing you ever saw?'

She took a moment to think. 'I remember a child being brought to me, badly burnt from the neck downwards. I couldn't cope with it, all I could do was wrap her in a clean sheet and take her to the hospital. She did recover but she was permanently scarred.'

'How did it happen?'

'I found out that the child had rolled into the fire. No one had saved her because the natives believed that if a child could not save itself, it was mentally deficient. They just let them die.'

'I don't believe it,' I exclaimed incredulously.

'I told the parents of the poor little child that if it ever happened again I would take the case to the Native Commissioner. Gerald and I were furious.'

'I don't blame you. How outrageous.'

'Outrageous! I had quite a reputation as a midwife, you know. Large doses of castor oil worked wonders at giving the baby a push in the right direction. I once helped deliver a baby in the back of a car,' she said as she closed her eyes. It was as if she were picturing the birth. 'The moment the little girl was born the boys and their families emerged from their huts clapping and shouting, "Motor carri. Motor carri." That's what they called the poor little girl you see. Motor car. The baby was brought to me the following day and I gave her a gift.'

At that point I realised how little I knew about Granny and all the incredible things she had done. Instead of thinking of her as a naïve girl as I had done in our earlier conversations when she confessed that she had not even known how babies were made, I was now seeing her as a powerful responsible woman whose help and advice were continually being sought. She was a mother, a doctor, a nurse, a midwife, an adviser, a carer and finally a wife, all rolled into one. And she was still in her early twenties.

'It was very sad,' she continued, 'because the little girl died shortly afterwards. Her mother had learnt from the house-boys that I fed my children with bottled milk. She got hold of a bottle and teat but she had no idea of the *care*...' Granny stressed, '...I took to boil the milk, watering it down to the right consistency. She had not sterilised the bottle and the child died of enteritis.'

'That must have been difficult to deal with? Such a waste of a life.'

'It was sickening. I couldn't always be there to watch their every move. Things did go terribly wrong at times. It was hard.'

'I don't know how you did it,' I shook my head. 'If I was suddenly confronted with a crowd of people with all kinds of things wrong with them I would panic like mad and probably run away.'

'Well, I did my best but I was no nurse. As long as I gave the boy with tummy ache something different to the boy with knee ache I told myself that I was doing all right!' she crowed with laughter. 'Elardie and George always complained of tummy upsets because they loved bicarbonate of soda. I mixed it with cochineal to make a 'wonderful pink muti'. They gulped it down!'

It reminded me of how much I used to love Benylin. I would constantly pretend to have a bad cough and drink the stuff out of the bottle. It was delicious. 'Did you enjoy the sessions Granny?' From the tone of her voice I imagined she had.

'I found their dependence upon me endearing. They were very fond of me. And I was fond of them.'

After breakfast we find Ambrose at the back gates in his dungarees and felt boots, scything the grass.

'Hello Ambrose,' Mum and Diana call to him. His round face bursts into a smile.

'We'd love to see your home, Ambrose,' I say. 'If that's OK?'

'Yes please,' he grins. He asks if we can go in the afternoon. I think he wants to warn the other families that we are coming. We nod and arrange to meet him at three o'clock.

Each wall of every hut is decorated with cuttings from magazines. Pictures of lavish interiors with swag curtains and beautiful box-pleated lampshades or pictures of grand tables lined with crystal glasses, silver cutlery, candlesticks and spidery green plants are pinned to the mud walls. Elsewhere, models in fur coats, hats and pointed shoes. Even Sandra

Bullock in a black wonder bra. Then I look at their table. It is bare and chipped. Hanging from the door like a hanging basket is a diet coke can used as a flower vase. A pair of worn red buckled shoes hang on one of the walls. There is one small bed to share between the whole family and on the other side of the hut they have a communal kitchen with a fire stove and a few ancient looking pots and pans.

'Why do they have all these pictures of things they'll never have?' I whisper to Diana.

'I've always imagined it's because the house-boys came back with descriptions of the Inkosika's house, with pictures on the walls, and they thought that this was the thing to do in their own homes,' she whispers back.

There isn't one spot of dirt or one thing out of place, and judging by the family's faces they are extremely proud to be showing us around their home. The only person who isn't happy is a baby boy. The moment we arrived his face scrunched into a tight ball and he started to wail, sobbing into his mother's back. I think children are 'spooked' by white people. Betty told us that if children are naughty their parents threaten them by saying, 'the white man will come and get you.' The baby's mother, aged eighteen, has a beautiful serene face. She's wearing a lime green dress, vivid against her dark skin.

There's quite a crowd circled around us. They are smiling and giggling. I don't think they know what to make of us in our squashed sunhats and sunglasses, with our funny voices. One of the school boys asks if he can have his photograph taken with his friend. Our visit has now turned into a photo shoot because everyone wants their picture taken. Diana is snapping away and when she runs out of film I take over. 'Can

I have you outside the doorway?' I ask two of the children. I want the photo to be set against the outside wall of the hut, colourfully decorated with brown flowers and leaves. Each hut is decorated with traditional patterns. I take a couple of pictures of two young girls with their proud mother. They are laughing and waving, sticking their thumbs up.

Ambrose taps Mum on the shoulder and asks if she'll take a picture of him in his Toyota. 'Of course, Ambrose,' she smiles. He sits in the front seat and pulls the biggest grin I have ever seen, his yellow teeth glistening. I'm dying to give him some Boots whitening toothpaste. 'Can I have one picture of baby?' asks the mother in the lime dress. The baby has calmed down, although his dark eyes still look confused and frightened. Mum and Diana find it upsetting that the young children are so scared and wary of us. The mother asks me how old I am and I tell her I'm twenty-six. She finds it hilarious that I am not married and have no children. When she finds out that my sister Helen, aged thirty-one, is not married and has no children, she continues to howl with laughter. Defensively, I tell myself that she won't have read *Bridget Jones's Diary*, so has no idea of a girl's life in England now.

One of the boys sits on an old tree trunk while Diana wipes the blood from his knee with a tissue found lurking at the bottom of her bag. They all giggle and point as they watch her helping him. In that moment, looking at Diana reminds me of a story Granny told me much later on, when they had been on the farm for nearly ten years.

June 1935
'Inkosikazi,' called one of the mothers, running towards

Margaret. 'Please Inkosikazi, please.'

Margaret followed the mother back to her kraal, dreading what she might find. Her confidence had plummeted after the recent death of George's mother-in-law. Margaret had been called out by George in the middle of the night only to find a beer party in progress and his mother drunk and snoring on the floor. Margaret stormed out of the hut saying, 'She's dead drunk George, leave her be.'

She awoke the next morning to the chorus, 'Mama's dead, she has been poisoned!' Margaret contacted the police to investigate her death. They reported that she had died from 'congestion in the lungs and drunkenness'. Margaret couldn't help thinking she was to blame. She had failed to tell George to move his mother into different sleeping positions throughout the night. The only consolation was that George appeared to be a new person. The funeral was rather a joyous occasion.

Margaret quickly turned her thoughts to the present again. She had to do something right. The woman led her into a hut where a girl of about ten lay on a mat, shivering. Margaret felt her forehead. It was burning and her neck was stiff. The entire family were standing around the girl, looking at Margaret intensely. Why do they depend on me, she asked herself. I'm no doctor. Mother, I wish you were with me. Sometimes I don't know what to do.

'I must go back to the house and ring the doctor immediately,' she told the anxious family.

'Doctor? Hospital?' The mother gazed at her with frightened eyes, 'Please help us, please.'

Margaret ran back to the house and dialled the doctor's number. It took a while to get through, but finally, 'I think it's meningitis, I can't be absolutely sure but I think you must come and see her,' she told the doctor.

Several hours later Margaret led the doctor through the bush to the kraal where they found the girl in the same state. The doctor examined her. 'We must get her to hospital now.'

A few days later Margaret sat in the mud hut drinking tea. The hut was empty apart from a pile of old blankets folded in the corner, a few rough shelves which housed old tins turned into mugs, and a chipped mirror on the wall. The family slept on the floor around the fire. They cleaned their hut immaculately. The polished floor was made from mud and ox blood and swept every day with an old broom made out of twigs.

'Inkosikazi.' The girl's mother handed Margaret a melon. 'Thank you,' she said. 'Spiwee is well. You made her better. She lives.'

As Margaret walked home, she turned round and saw Spiwee's mother still standing outside the hut. She tentatively waved and Margaret waved back. 'Mother, I think you would be proud of me,' she smiled.

With the melon cradled in her arms like a baby she began to walk home.

'I continued to visit the young girl until her strength returned. It was such a joy seeing her recover. I think it was the one time when I felt I had made a real difference,' Granny had told me. 'The melon was quite delicious too! Gerald and I did enjoy it.'

Later we spoke again about the death of George's mother-in-law.

'She was so tiresome and always whining away. I was quite thankful she was dead.'

'Granny! What a thing to say!' I exclaimed with a shriek of shocked laughter. She had suddenly turned from a heroine to a bad woman.

'Oh,' she shrugged, 'well I can say that now can't I? We burnt her hut down and that was that.'

As we finally say goodbye to the families they curtsey and shake our hands. We promise to send them the photographs and they curtsey again. I wish they wouldn't curtsey, it's not right. Besides, I am the one who feels humbled.

CHAPTER NINETEEN

It is early evening and we are about to drive to Spring Grange to stay for three nights at the farm where Granny's old neighbours, the Mitchells, used to live. The farm is now owned by the Mitchells' granddaughter, Barbara, and her husband Peter Hubert. Barbara is Granny's goddaughter.

There was a very heavy storm last night and Fred has offered to drive our car to the Hilda's Kraal Road. Ambrose will accompany us in the truck in order to take Fred back.

'You can go with Ambrose,' I say to Diana. Mum promptly sits in the car too. Diana climbs into the truck. Ambrose looks like a frightened rabbit as he sets off first.

The road is slimy and churned up by the neighbour's tractors. If we were on our own, the Mazda would end up in the ditch in no time. As the truck turns the corner to go down to the bridge over the drift it starts to slide crabwise down the hill. Ambrose just about negotiates it and with a mighty acceleration he manages to get up the other side.

'Your turn now Fred! You can do it!' I shout from the back seat. Mum is deadly quiet, her worried face squashed up against the windscreen. 'Oh Fred, I don't like this at all,' she mutters, shifting in her seat. Fred looks far too confident to worry, he has done this journey countless times. When I remember the stories Granny told me about the road conditions it makes our journey seem pathetically tame.

'There was one time when Diana was six weeks old and I had to take her to the doctor,' she had started. 'When we were in Bulawayo a huge storm broke over us and driving home the roads were muddy and skiddy. We reached the second Umguza drift but the water was well above the danger mark, so much so that we had to turn round and go back to Bulawayo. However, the first drift which we had managed to cross before was now flooded. Gerald would not let me go in the car because he was scared it might get washed away. I had to carry Diana on the swing bridge with only a single wire strand as a handrail. I clutched the baby tightly with one hand and steadied myself on the handrail with the other although this was difficult because my legs were quivering like jelly. I tried not to look down to the turbulent river below, nor the shaking bridge beneath my feet. It was like being on a tightrope and I should have taken off my shoes. That bridge was only a hundred yards long but it seemed like a mile. When I reached the end I could barely stand or walk.'

So really, we mustn't com... shit. SHIT. The car is zigzagging from side to side in a drunken fashion. There are places in the road where the crest of the road is a good eighteen inches higher than the tyre tracks and we have to drive with one wheel on the bump and the other on the edges of the road. We slither around another corner. Diana looks back at us sliding down the road at a forty five degree angle, Mum's anxious face still peering through the windscreen. Is a visit to Spring Grange worth all of this?

Finally we reach the tarmac road. My legs are shaking. I hear Diana applauding Ambrose. Ambrose saunters to the car and proudly tells Fred that the 'white missus squeaked a bit.'

Spring Grange is approximately nine miles from M'Coben, on the road to Bulawayo. I wonder what Barbara and Peter Hubert will be like. Fred and Betty know the Huberts well.

Fred told us horrific stories about the time of the Dissidents in the early 1980s – when disaffected Matabele killed off white people in a vain attempt to draw world attention to their unsatisfactory position in the political settlement under the Lancaster House Agreement – and about the atrocities of the Fifth Brigade sent down by Mugabe ostensibly to quell the dissidents and search out Nkomo, leader of the Matabele. Fred told us how brave Peter was in protecting his farm workers from the Fifth Brigade during this time.

There was one occasion when half of Peter's farm workers and their families had been abducted. Peter set off to find them and came up against a whole group of his men, stripped to the waist, crammed together like sardines, kneeling with their heads pressed to the ground. 'These savages were walking on Peter's men, beating their flesh with their cudgels,' Fred described. The children were in two separate groups, the women were herded together in the bushes. Peter was so furious that he did not have time to be scared. 'He shouted and screamed in protest and three hours later he was able to leave with all of them,' Fred said.

We take a turning to the left signed to 'Spring Grange' with a picture of a smiling bull mounted in a tyre. It reminds me of the laughing cow, advertising cheese. Mum hops out and opens the gate. The road is bumpy and lined with brown cows who are staring at us. Eventually they move when they see that the car is not going to stop for them. I wonder what Peter and Barbara will be doing when we arrive?

I remember Granny telling me that the Mitchells had 'called on them' while she was experimenting in the kitchen making some brandysnaps. They were still camping in the tin huts and tent. 'We were living in such a mess that I think the biscuits surprised and impressed Mrs Mitchell!' Granny laughed. She went on to tell me that the only young people in the district were the Mitchell daughters, Evelyn and Ursula, aged eighteen and twenty. They had been in Africa since the turn of the century. Mr Mitchell used to be a bank manager in Bulawayo but was retired. Mrs Mitchell was short and stout. Their home was beautiful, built in red sandstone. They had a wonderful view of the valley which teemed with guinea-fowl, francolin, quail, sand-grouse, buck of all kinds including large kudu and sable. Mr Mitchell had stocked his farm with Hereford cattle and built up a valuable herd. Mrs Mitchell gave Margaret advice about housekeeping problems, gardening and cooking while Mr Mitchell taught them a lot about the handling of native labour. They also introduced them to the other neighbours. Between them all they organised tennis parties, suppers, plays and dances at the weekends. 'It was really great fun as I was not introduced to any real duds and I could dance with whom I chose,' Margaret wrote to her mother after one party.

I know the Huberts' home will be lovely because Granny said that she was permanently 'green with envy' every time they visited the Mitchells, realising it would take them years to make M'Coben as attractive. 'Do you remember Spring Grange?' I ask Mum and Diana.

'Yes, I used to think it was so luxurious,' Diana drew out the 'so' like a long exhalation from a cigarette. 'Mrs Mitchell used to prepare little crystal bowls of roasted monkey nuts on the dining table. I adored going there. It was also where I was christened.' She smiles as if she is about to tell us another

176

story. 'I remember my father telling me how Anne was so bored by the Bishop of Rhodesia's prayers that she had said in the middle of them, "Why does that funny man keep on talking?"'

We gradually turn one more corner, go through a gate and park around the back of the house. A large shaggy dog limps towards us, hopping on one leg, followed by a highly charged brown Labrador puppy, Hulabaloo. A slight man dressed in surprisingly short shorts with legs as thin as spaghetti walks towards us. He is white-haired and very brown, his knees are wrinkled. 'Hi,' he beams, 'welcome to Spring Grange. I'm Peter.' He takes my small suitcase. Straight ahead of me at the end of the garden is a large wiry sculpture of a woman on a swing.

We walk up some steps and on to the verandah which looks out on to a garden filled with flowers of every colour. I like the effect of allowing the flowers and plants to grow wild on their own. I'm sure it's what my garden would look like if I had one. Barbara appears. She is small and plump with short grey wavy hair and a warm smile. She gives us a quick tour of the house and shows us our rooms. Barbara tells us that Spring Grange burnt down in 1972 due to faulty wiring. The Mitchells' daughter, Evelyn, (Barbara's aunt) was living there at the time and after the fire she moved to a small cottage nearby. 'When Evelyn died she passed the farm on to me,' Barbara explains. 'It took us seventeen years before we could afford to rebuild Spring Grange. We built it in exactly the same shape and with the same red sandstone.'

'Seventeen years?' I repeat in disbelief.

'Yes, and during all those years we lived in a row of small

shacks at the back of the ruins of the house.'

Over supper, a casserole of stewed francolin – I am not sure what kind of bird or animal that is – they tell us that they farm Hereford cattle crossed with Brahmans. Over the years they have worked hard to get to where they are today, owners of a thriving cattle ranch.

The following morning is grey and the wind is howling. I imagine this is a 'makasa,' like Granny described. The dust is flying. I feel very sore. I sit at the edge of the bed and try to stretch. I hate this time of morning. I can't describe this pain. All I know is that the RA can rear its ugly head after a night's sleep to remind me it's still there. Inside I want to scream. I drag myself to the bathroom and run some hot water for a bath.

Spring Grange is not quite how I imagined it to be. When Barbara was giving us a tour I noticed that it is an extraordinary mixture of sophistication and primitiveness. There are many fine objects, carvings, sculptures, books and pictures but the plumbing is dreadful. We think that they have salvaged the baths, basins and pipes from the ruins and simply reinstated them. I couldn't flush the loo last night and I still can't this morning, damn it. I try again and realise I'm going to have to report the fault to Peter. Diana suddenly knocks on the door rapidly. 'I'm in here,' I shout back irritably.

'Can I come in?' she asks behind the door. Her bedroom is upstairs in the main house. She tells me that her loo is completely defunct and 'can I use yours?'

Barbara and Peter more than make up for the not-so-brilliant plumbing by asking us if we would like to be taken around the farm. Barbara has a farmers' meeting in Bulawayo but Peter is free. We dress in thick woolly jumpers and Peter courageously lifts me up and puts me on to the front seat of his Toyota. As he shows us around, it is clear he is deeply proud of their farm. Just from the way he describes each building, their workers and their routine, it is obvious that the farm means everything to him. 'Barbara's grandfather bought Spring Grange in 1904,' he informs us, 'and in fact many of today's employees are also grandsons from workers of those days. It feels like they are our race relations! I like the fact that they have stayed on. It shows that they think of this place as their home too.'

He shows us the site where they are building a school and community centre for the African families with a football pitch for the boys and girls. On the way back to the house he takes a detour to deliver mealie-meal and salt to the African families. 'I made it a rule with the staff that they must bring their families with them. No one wants to be apart from their families, it's miserable. Also I'm sure it reduces the number of cases of AIDS.' I stay in the car but watch Peter as he introduces Diana and Mum to three men. 'Barry at M'Coben,' I hear Diana saying and there are great smiles of recognition and shaking of hands. One of the boys who remembered Granny at M'Coben proceeds to teach Diana how to do the Matabele handshake. I overhear him asking her where she lives. When she tells him he says, 'At least you have a proper government.' He then withdraws his hand with defiance and fear, as if someone might have heard him and then go on to denounce him as a traitor for criticising his country.

Over the next two days Peter and Barbara talk a lot about the politics of the country. There is to be a referendum very soon to vote 'yes' or 'no' to a new draft Constitution which, amongst many things, gives Mugabe unlimited powers. The forthcoming election is scheduled for March 2000 and Mugabe is trying to bolster his fading popularity by threatening to seize all white-owned farms, stating that the UK Government is expected to pay compensation to the white men, as penance for the white man's theft of the country in the first place.

Peter and Barbara are due to go to America shortly, they have saved up for this trip. 'How can we go when everything is so uncertain? When Mugabe is threatening to take over white farms?' Barbara asks us. 'I can't imagine going away and returning to find our farm has been snatched from us. Where would we go? We have nowhere else, this is our home.' She looks at Peter. 'I don't think we should go.'

Peter shakes his head wearily, 'We've talked about this. We haven't seen our family in years. We need a holiday.'

Fred and Betty had also talked to us about the uncertain future in Zimbabwe. Over breakfast one morning Fred shook his head cynically. 'I'm not sure if the referendum will take place at all. No one knows where or when to vote, well no one in the country districts at any rate.' This appeared to be true. When Diana had asked Ambrose whether he was going to vote 'yes' or 'no' in the referendum he had looked at her blankly. It was clear that he did not know what she was talking about.

As Barbara and Peter talk to us I feel for them. How frightening it is to be faced with the possibility of Mugabe and his followers invading your home. If I was in their shoes, and I can hardly imagine confronting such a problem, half of me would want to flee the country straightaway. The other half would hope to be like Barbara and Peter – brave enough to face the inevitable problems ahead. Why should they give up everything they have worked so hard for, especially when they are building schools and trying to help their workers? I pray Mugabe's threats come to nothing.

We watch the sunset. Diana points to the Paradise Flycatchers which flit in and out of a large acacia tree in front of us. As Diana says, the peace and beauty of the scene contrast forcibly with the picture in our minds of pain and terror. 'That is Africa,' she says, 'this wild, brutal, beautiful country.'

CHAPTER TWENTY

We have just left Spring Grange after a frustrating morning. It took us two hours to find the car keys. We thought that Hulabaloo might have eaten them, but eventually they were found in the side pocket of Diana's handbag. She blames the malaria pills. Then, desperate to leave, we reached the car only to find an army of black ants crawling up the seats and on the floor, and under the seat belts. I screamed, (my days seem to be punctuated with little screams) and Mum asked Barbara if she had any killer ant spray. The culprit was Mum who had left a salad roll on the front seat. She too, blamed the malaria pills.

For the next three nights we are staying at a bed and breakfast called 'Macalister's,' on the outskirts of Bulawayo. As we drive into Bulawayo, 'a deadly little town,' as Margaret called it, we decide to stop and have a look around the shops and markets.

Bulawayo is unrecognisable to Mum and Diana, except for the wide roads and a few buildings like 'Meikles,' a big department store. 'But that's the way it should be Alice,' Diana says as we take a wrong turn, 'it's hard to get my bearings because I haven't been here for fifty-one years.' Mum nods. I ask them whether they shouldn't blame the malaria pills.

Bulawayo is quite westernised. After being on the farm, coming here is like stepping into another world. I pop into the Bulawayo Centre, an indoor shopping complex, and buy some CD's. The Africans appear to like stamping everything. They stamp the cash receipt and my hand as I leave. I also notice that many of the men hold hands, I suppose as a sign of friendship rather than anything else. Finally, before joining Mum and Diana, I go into a bookshop called Kingstons. As I am scanning the shelves, I spot my cousin Bella Pollen's book, *All About Men* on one of the front bookshelves, coincidentally next to a book called, *All you need to know about sex*. *All about Men*, really isn't all about men, I think to myself. It's more about the fashion world. I must tell her that her book is next to a sex manual.

Bella and I once talked about how titles hardly ever reflected what the book was about. Someone in the publishing world suggested my first book, *A Will to Win*, should be called, *Down the rabbit-hole*. Why?

We are eating lunch at the National Art Gallery, having just been to the market. Mum and Diana bought some doilies with beads to put over milk jugs to stop flies buzzing in. They seem extraordinarily pleased with their buys.

The market pavements were lined with a mass of carved wooden animals, linen, beaded necklaces and bracelets, the stall-holders desperate for us to turn browsing into buying. A man followed us all the way out of the market and down the street holding some giraffe salad spoons, saying with a glint in his eye, 'Good price just for you ladies.' At this stage I was in the wheelchair as I was tired and sore from all the previous walking. Mum and Diana took it in turns bumping the chair up and down the pavements. We hadn't planned to eat at the art gallery but it was the nearest place to escape.

As we finish lunch we try to work out how much we owe. We cannot seem to get to grips with the currency and how much we should tip the waiters. Compared to England, everything is relatively cheap for us. We have eaten lunch, had glasses of wine, coffees and ice cream, all for about £5.

'Good price, just for you,' the same man says, now offering us a wooden hippopotamus. As we say no again, I suddenly feel guilty that we have just had a lovely lunch and this poor man probably still hasn't sold anything.

The weather is overcast as we drive out of Bulawayo, but the bougainvillaea trees and the flame trees with their striking orange flowers brighten the roads. Incidentally, every road seems to be called 'Robert Mugabe Way'. On our way to Macalister's, we pass through Hillside which is one of the most popular suburbs of Bulawayo. This is where Diana was born. In Margaret's letters she had described how worried she was that she could not have another baby. 'A dreadful disappointment this month again as I had really begun to hope number two had started as I was several days late.' There was great relief and joy when she discovered that she was finally pregnant again. She described how she and Gerald had met Sir Boucher Wrey, Director of the South African Company, at Government House. When he discovered that she was pregnant with her second child, he offered to lend Margaret his home at Hillside for the birth.

There's a complex of shops and the place is throbbing with people and cars. Granny told me that the houses in Hillside could be counted on one hand and that the road from the town was a very rough dirt track.

I lean through the gap between the passenger and front seat of the car and talk to Diana about her birth. The birth that haunted Granny.

M'Coben, complete with the addition of the sitting room to the left

Gerald with Diana, 1929

Relaxing on the verandah at M'Coben

First cousins Christopher and Julian Petherick paddling with Anne in Cornwall

Anne and Diana feeding a baby reedbuck

Diana and Anne, bathing in the reservoir at M'Coben

Margaret presenting Patricia to Anne and Diana, July 1932

Raden with Patricia

Patricia and Gill

Tony Coombe, 1933, Zambezi Trip

Swimming at M'Coben

Diana and Jenefer at St Cross, Winchester, 1936

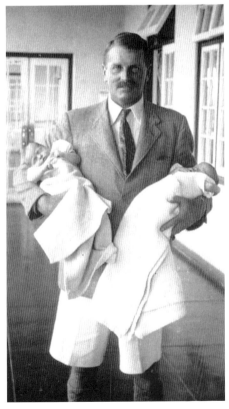

Gerald with the newborn twins, November 1939

Margaret in the garden at M'Coben

Gerald and Margaret with Patricia, Gill and the twins, just before Gerald joined the Rhodesia Regiment, 1939

Raden with Richard and Pam

*Richard and Pam at Bonnie Blink,
America*

*Margaret with the twins, Cape Cod,
1941*

Richard (front, far left) and Pam (front, far right) at Bonnie Blink, Spring 1942

THE COLONEL OF A HIGHLAND REGIMENT WITH HIS STAFF IN A WEAPON PIT WHICH THE JOCKS CAPTURED. IT IS SERVING AS THE BATTALION HEADQUARTERS.

Gerald, with pipe, in a bomb crater, Battle of Tobruk

Above, homecoming celebrations
Right, partying and brewing beer

Margaret's brain felt more cow-like as the days drew nearer to the birth. 'I am looking forward to rejuvenation after it's all over, it can't be much longer than three weeks now. I miss my Anne. She is so funny. She kneels beside me when we say our prayers and begins, "Dear Goddy," and then continually asks for a baby brother, "Send me a baby brother!" I have to try so hard not to laugh into her face! Well, I must stop this letter. My news is really quite snoring mother, I suppose I'm becoming a potato. But you don't know how much I love writing to you. Other letters go to the wall, but yours never will.'

Margaret leaned back against the pillow. She hoped that next time she wrote home she would be telling her mother that she had had a baby boy. 'Dear God, send me a boy,' she prayed for the final time.

It was a warm October day. Gerald was in the orchard inspecting the vine trees. The peaches, plums, apricots, apples, pear and mulberry trees had arrived in July and Gerald and Margaret longed for the day when their fruit would be ripe for picking. They had planted over three hundred trees. Orange and citrus trees were planted in the orchard to the left of the house. To irrigate them Gerald had to scoop out a ring some nine inches from the tree and a few inches deep and pour four gallons of water on to each tree. As soon as the water had soaked in, the basin had to be filled in again. Although it was hard work this kind of irrigation lasted a fortnight.

Jacaranda trees had been planted around the house. They were Margaret's favourite because they reminded her of English wisteria with its lovely mauve flower. The main job had been planting hundreds of blue gum and cypress trees. The next plan was to build a reservoir by the orchard to make irrigation easier but also to be used as a swimming pool for the children.

Gerald missed talking to Margaret about the day and playing backgammon or bezique with her in the evenings. When he next visited Hillside he would tell her that the chickens had escaped from their runs and that a rhino was seen on one of the neighbouring farms. The latest news on the whereabouts of the rhino were that he had meandered off into the bush and was lost somewhere opposite their house or towards the distant hills. Gerald smiled to himself, thinking how close it could possibly be.

The phone rang. With any luck it would be the doctor with the happy news that the baby was born. He longed for a boy. It was a call from the nurse to tell him to get to Hillside at once, the baby was on its way. Margaret liked Gerald to be with her the moment the birth was over.

Hillside was two miles out of Bulawayo. Gerald thumped the steering wheel, 'If I worked for the government I'd do something about these bloody dirt roads, nothing gets done in this country.' He swore loudly as another mass of thorny bush obstructed his way.

After a hazardous drive, he found Margaret as peaceful as a queen on her bed. Nothing had happened, and nothing looked as if it was going to happen. He sank into a chair thankful he had arrived in time.

The doctor turned up the following morning and examined Margaret. 'The baby is facing the wrong way round,' he told her. As he left, he told Gerald that there was no indication, in his opinion, of the baby's imminent arrival. 'Ring me up in Bulawayo if anything happens, I can get here in no time.'

'Did I tell you brother Willie and Helena have had a son? They're going to call him Jacob,' Margaret told Gerald.

'That's wonderful news,' Gerald agreed. 'How are you feeling?' he asked calmly. No sooner had he asked the question when Margaret's face changed colour.

Gerald shook the telephone in despair. He could slaughter the wretched officials at the Exchange at Bulawayo with the greatest pleasure, it was damnable. Margaret was not making a sound but he knew she was holding in the screaming pain. The baby had twisted round and was coming now. NOW. Sister Roux was helping as much as she could but had no pain relief to offer. No anaesthetic. Gerald realised it was no use trying the phone any longer, he would have to drive into Bulawayo and hunt down the doctor. He could be at any one of the houses carrying out his morning visits. Gerald set off, not knowing where to begin looking for him. Blast the man. It was a BAD show.

She shouldn't be going through this alone, without her family, no friends, not even the damn doctor, Gerald thought, his hands firm on the steering wheel. If we were in England she'd be in a proper hospital and have her mother with her. Instead she's got no one, and is stuck in some remote house with one solitary midwife and no pain relief. I won't forgive myself, he pledged firmly to himself. What have I done to Margaret bringing her here?

After the longest hour he hoped he ever had to endure, just imagining what Margaret was going through, Gerald caught the doctor tucking into an early lunch at the hospital after finishing his morning rounds of private houses. Luckily Tom Meikle, the owner of many hotels and big general stores, had spotted him walking in that direction. Gerald set off with the doctor back to Hillside, but the dirt tracks were hopeless in emergencies. They hit another rough hole in the road, the car taking another knock.

Gerald glanced at the doctor, wanting him to say something, apologise at the very least. The doctor's face was pinched, far from the carefree manner he had shown that morning. Gerald found his silence painful. It looked as if every inch of his body was tight. His shoulders were hunched unnaturally. Gerald imagined that he did not know what to say or he was too scared to say anything at all. When he had stormed into the hospital, swept the doctor's plate away and picked him up by the scruff of his neck and shouted, 'Margaret is having the baby NOW,' Gerald had never seen a man look as distressed.

As they sprinted up the stairs, Gerald sweating in his khaki shorts and shirt, they heard a baby's cry. He found Margaret sore and exhausted, holding the baby in her arms. 'It's too late,' she told the doctor, who approached her, equipped with the anaesthetic. He nodded sympathetically and mumbled how sorry he was.

Gerald rushed to her, his heart overflowing with pride and relief. Margaret smiled weakly and held his hand to tell him everything was fine. He looked at them both. It was the perfect picture and Gerald hoped more than ever that the new baby would make Margaret feel more settled on the farm. He kissed her forehead hiding the tears in his eyes. The most important thing was that both she and the baby were safe and well.

He looked across at Sister Roux who was taking a moment to recover from the hard work of delivering the baby on her own. She smiled at Gerald, thinking he had to be one of the most handsome men she had ever come across. Margaret is lucky, she thought to herself. Why aren't there more men like him around? Gerald smiled back at her, his eyes telling her how eternally grateful he was.

'It's a girl,' Margaret cried, reaching to hold his shaking hand.

Gerald hadn't even thought to ask what sex it was.

'I think we should call her Diana.'

Gerald knelt on the floor, held a little hand and peered into big blue eyes. 'Hello Diana,' he said.

We finally arrive at Macalister's. We are shown to our little thatched chalets.

It's early evening and time for a shower. The bathroom has a shower, loo and basin and the plumbing is new and shiny. The water is hot! There are no signs of spiders! Feeling very refreshed and clean I open the mini-bar and am delighted to see an assortment of drinks. I make myself a vodka and pineapple and sigh with happiness hearing the ice crackle. I then switch on the television. There's more news about the forthcoming referendum. The telephone suddenly rings. This place feels so modern. I feel totally at home here. There's even a little mint chocolate on my pillow, I think as I watch Mum pick up the telephone. Hurrah. I like it here. Mum is listening to an irate traveller who has lost all his luggage at Harare airport. In the background she can hear a much more interesting conversation about potted plants. Fred warned us about the telephones. 'When you ring a number don't expect to get through to the person intended. Try to ring Bulawayo Airport and you start chatting to a nice person from Johannesburg,' he cackled.

The telephone business reminds me of the letters Granny wrote home about the advent of their telephone in January 1927. 'We are feeling fearfully civilised mother. We can ring up Bulawayo at any time and order things from the stores. We are on the party line and have specially allotted ringing up times, M'Coben is at 10.20am and 4.00pm. If any neighbour wants to catch us they have to switch on their telephone and wait until we come on to the line. Incidentally everyone can listen in and hear other fellows' conversations! Gerald was talking to the Government poultry expert who was advising him to buy Rhode Island Red chickens. 'I won't tell you anything more just now, because I am sure Joe is listening in,' Gerald said as he heard the tell-tale click of the receiver. Hardly were these words out of his mouth when a familiar voice spoke up, 'Sure, I am doing nothing of the kind!'

The telephone rings again and Dad is on the line telling Mum she has a parking ticket which has gone up to £80. Mum knew already but decided not to tell him. Dad suggests writing back to the council explaining that his wife has gone to Africa and he has no idea when, or indeed if, she is returning. We both get changed and I go to find Diana. She's talking to a few of the workers outside.

'I was born here, in Bulawayo,' I overhear Diana tell them, 'but I have not returned for over fifty years.' One of the girls shakes her hand warmly to welcome her back.

'It still feels very much like home,' Diana says. 'I was born at Hillside.'

As I watch I can't help smiling. I know I would be proud too.

CHAPTER TWENTY-ONE

Mum, Diana and I arrive at Bulawayo Airport and head for the upstairs balcony. I am so excited. At last! I am going to be with some young people! Helen and James arrive today by plane from Johannesburg. They have spent the last two weeks in the Cape. We watch the heavy rain clouds gathering and circling the city some miles away. From this vantage point we will be able to see the plane come in and land, and hopefully we will spot Helen and James emerging.

'Here it comes,' Mum says. We lean against the rails of the balcony, determined that they should see us when they walk out of the plane.

Two tall figures in sun-glasses stride across the tarmac. Even from here I can see how tanned they are. How unfair. There's been nothing but rain here.

'Wahoo,' Mum shouts as she waves her arms.

I try to negotiate the stairs as quickly as I can. I've got so much I want to tell Helen and James. I haven't seen them in nearly three weeks.

They come through the doors with wide smiles, trailing a mountain of luggage behind them. James is pushing at least two crates of South African wine. Trying to work out how we are all going to fit in the car is like taking part in the Krypton Factor quiz. Eventually it is decided that I have to lie across Helen and Mum in the back seat as we make our way back to Macalister's. 'No marriage proposal from James yet?' I whisper.

'Ssh,' Helen gently hits me.

Helen and James are tired and have a rest in their chalet before supper. I decide to sit outside on the balcony and read over some more of Margaret's letters. I want to read the letters she wrote after her parents' first visit to the farm. Seeing Helen and James has made me realise how special Margaret's first reunion with her mother and father must have been. Her letters reveal how much she craved to see them.

17 April 1927
'I almost burst with the longing to see you yesterday. It must have been a communion of hearts and minds, because my worst moment was at 10.00 – (8am at Longford) just the time that you were all at church up at Alderbury. And then I suddenly felt quite uplifted and different. There is a wonderful wireless between us, I know there is.'

Granny's parents came out in February 1928, nearly two years after Margaret and Gerald had begun living at M'Coben. Margaret and Gerald had so much to show them: Anne who was now four years old; Diana who was four months; they would see their home! I think I would have exploded with anticipation and excitement. I get carried away showing Mum or my friends my latest Jigsaw outfit. I try to imagine how that day must have been.

'Mother you don't know how we look forward to your coming. It is too lovely that you are both going to see our house for the first time together. I lose count of months out here, it could easily be June, January or August for me! All the months seem much the same – but February won't!'

The week leading up to their arrival, Margaret spent every day springcleaning the house to make the welcome as homely as it could be. Elardie washed and ironed the linen, bedspreads and the furniture covers. Each room had its own curtains and pretty coloured chintzes over petrol boxes for tables. They had two extra chairs and a table in the dining-room. Gerald had made the dining-room sideboard from deal wood bought in Bulawayo and all the cupboards were made out of boxes. They had built a rondavel[1] for her father's dressing room.

At last the morning arrived and Gerald drove to Bulawayo to collect them off the mail train. Margaret stayed at home, restlessly watching the time.

In a few hours she would see her parents, she thought blissfully. The letters they had written every week to one another would now mean so much more. Her mother would be able to see the farm, the garden, their house, the new verandah and perhaps the biggest luxury of all, the bathroom she had written of. Gerald had built it in a separate building a yard or so away from their bedroom door. The walls were bright green, and rather than storing the linen and blankets in tin boxes, Margaret had proper big cupboards made out of wood with shelves and doors. Gerald had also made a wonderful boiler which was nicknamed, 'the Cathedral'. It consisted of two fifty-gallon drums of water built into a brick oven with enough space for big logs to be pushed in underneath to make a fire. Considering Gerald's primitive knowledge of plumbing, working on the basic theory that water runs downhill, he has worked wonders, she thought with pride. He had piped the hot and cold water to the bath and there was also a waste pipe which went through a wall, flowing into a

---

[1] Small hut

large tank used for watering the garden. The boys scooped the water out of the tank with small cans for watering the plants and flowers.

Njoni, the deaf and dumb boy and Paul, his helper, had been hard at work building a cobbled path in the garden. They had also gravelled the 'sweep' which was the entrance to the house and levelled out the gravelled drive which made the approach to the house much tidier. Surely they would be impressed?

As Gerald was approaching Bulawayo, he was apprehensive about the forthcoming visit. At the same time he was relieved for Margaret's sake that she would at last see her parents again. He could not deny to himself that she missed them and that at times she craved to be back in England. As he and Margaret became more settled and established on the farm, there was more time for homesickness.

There had been one blank week when Margaret had not received a letter from her mother. She had sat quietly in the bedroom looking at old photographs. When he joined her she immediately put on a brave face and brushed the photos aside. He caught a glimpse of a photograph of her and Barty reading a book together, Anthony sitting on the floor. There was another picture of Margaret outside the front door at Longford, dressed in her riding habit and cap with a riding-crop in her hand, standing proudly next to Ginger, her horse. He was certain she had been crying. At times like this, he reproached himself for taking her so far away.

At other times of course, when they were both blissfully happy, he would reassure himself that he had made the right decision to live and bring up a family in Rhodesia. I know we can make a go of it here, he thought to himself, we can live cheaply and make money on the farm. I miss Norfolk and the river. I miss my family, but not in the same way that Margaret misses hers. I don't feel the wrench a mother and daughter feel when parted. He took a deep breath, wondering when his parents last wrote. He could not remember.

Margaret's parents must feel some kind of resentment towards me for taking their daughter away, he thought, but I want them to leave knowing they can trust me to look after her and provide for the family. I want them to see the hard work I have put into the farm, especially with the tobacco. I have planted more than ten acres and the expert said it was the finest crop he'd seen in the district. He said that I should make some decent money from it. I want Margaret's father to see the potential of M'Coben just as I did. To see how it could grow into something prosperous. I want them both to be proud of me too.

Gerald spotted them instantly, two pale upright figures. Margaret's father was much thinner than Gerald remembered. Mother wore a beige hat shielding her delicate skin, a cotton dress, a line of delicate pearls and brown buckled shoes. Father was in a travelling suit. He still had his thick moustache and those vivid eyes which showed his love of life. Just as Margaret's did.

Gerald kissed his mother-in-law and then turned to Margaret's father. 'Gerald, how wonderful to see you,' he heard, their hands clutched in a warm handshake. The luggage was brought to the car.

'We often had visitors at Longford,' Margaret was telling Anne. 'If it was a favourite guest Barty and I would call out from the nursery window to them, "When are you going away?" It probably sounded rude.'

Anne laughed.

'What we really meant was, "How long are you staying?"'

Margaret stopped as she heard the engine of the car. She rushed outside, Anne and Shadow the dog running after her. Anne was wearing her best hat which Margaret had made for her. Mother stepped gracefully out of the car and walked towards the house, taking in the surroundings. She looked hot and tired from the journey. Margaret could not hold the restraint any longer and flung her arms around her mother in an unusual display of affection. Mother hugged her back, and they held each other, neither one withdrawing. Gerald turned to Father but, seeing some tears quickly walked away, calling Elardie and George to help take in the luggage. He wanted Margaret to be alone with her parents. She deserved this moment after waiting so long.

Two weeks later

It was a cool evening, and Margaret and her mother were sitting out on the newly built verandah. Gerald was with Margaret's father, walking around the farm.

'He seems better,' Margaret commented, referring to her father, 'I know you've been anxious about his health, Mother.' It was strange how formal Margaret felt with her mother. When she wrote home she felt less inhibited about her emotions.

'I think the warmth and sunshine help him,' Mother replied, 'and he loved visiting the Victoria Falls.'

Margaret smiled to herself, not wanting to remind Mother that they had both asked, 'What can one do looking at a dull waterfall for three days?' when Gerald had suggested they took the train from Nyamandhlovu up to the Victoria Falls. They continued to talk about the family, going through each brother and sister again. 'I shall feel quite dowdy and out of fashion when I next go home,' Margaret laughed. 'I've forgotten what it's like to dress up and go to dances! My dear, if it wasn't for the clothes, the hats and the lovely Liberty materials you send me for myself and the children, we'd have very dud outfits. I used to love the hats we wore as children. The ones I make are rather floppy affairs.'

Mother smiled. 'They started the week bright white, starched and stiff, with the piece of elastic around the chin. By the end of the week they were pushed to the back of your neck and soft and floppy.'

'We did love playing in the garden,' Margaret sighed nostalgically.

'You loved to accompany me on my evening visits, especially if the strawberries were in season,' Mother added. 'It cost me many lost trowels and forks!'

They talked about Margaret wanting another baby and Margaret was told she needed to put on a bit of weight first, she looked too thin. Then they returned to talk happily about Gerald and her father, Mother saying how relieved she was that the trip was benefiting him. He had been having worrying problems with his chest and breathing. The day he had arrived he looked painfully thin and tired. However the climate obviously suited him. 'Place of Ghosts' had breathed new life into him.

It was nearly Diana's bed time. She was a healthy chubby baby with tufts of hair that stuck out like a cockatoo, pink cheeks, a turned up nose and fair eyelashes and eyebrows like Gerald's.

'Do you read to them?' Mother asked.

'Gerald is on duty tonight. When the children are older I will teach them to read and write from home, just like you did with us Mother. I'll teach them history and geography, arithmetic and French. I remember that lovely book, *Reading without Tears*, that you read to us.' Margaret could still picture her and Barty sitting at a small square table, her mother holding up a black and white drawing on the top of the page.

'I remember. I still have that book.' Mother looked down to Diana. 'She has your eyes. She's charming. Anne is too, though I hardly recognised her.' Anne had shot up in height over the past two years. She was like Gerald, tall and thin. 'She's grown up quickly,' Mother continued, 'and she can draw beautifully. She showed me some of her pictures. She has a great gift, you must be proud of her.' She looked away, her eyes downcast, unsure whether she should admit what she was wanting to say. Finally, she confessed, 'I have missed you.'

Margaret wanted to reach out and hold her hand.

There was an understanding moment of silence, eventually broken by Gerald and her father talking animatedly as they returned from their evening walk.

I remember the conversations Granny and I had about her parents' visit.

'I did so enjoy having them,' Granny said. 'The companionship was wonderful.'

'I can imagine. It must have been lonely at times.'

She buttoned up again, crossing her arms defensively. 'I was never lonely. Gerald and I were too busy,' she stated firmly.

I decided not to press it, what was the point? 'Tell me more about their visit.'

'My mother looked after Diana and Anne for a day to let me go into Bulawayo. When I got back she was worn out. You see she had never looked after children before. I looked after the children entirely by this stage, the nanny had gone. It wasn't a country where you wanted white servants. It was no life for them. I once caught the nanny smoking Gerald's cigars too,' she huffed.

I think half the reason for wanting Nanny to go was that Granny was quite intolerant of people too. Even in one letter she told her mother how she despaired of the young, when she was only twenty-six herself – my age! She wrote in a letter home, 'Gerald and I love our peaceful evenings when we can read or just sit quiet – but we can't for the moment as Nanny is with us, and her ceaseless prattle almost does us in! She plays the gramophone non-stop and always wants to be going out dancing.'

The other half reason was to save money. 'Gerald and I talk about our money problems together, there is no veil drawn between us. We are both aware that we could be horribly overdrawn if we are not careful. By sending Nanny away we are saving £10 a month. We are determined to make money here somehow. It's silly that the money we do make goes into Nanny's wages.'

'Your father was very happy staying with you wasn't he?'

'He adored M'Coben,' Granny sighed with total conviction.

'He was as happy as a sandboy. He was tremendously interested in the farm activities,' she continued, 'he particularly loved watching the well-trained span of oxen working the land.'

'Who trained the oxen?'

'We called them the "boss-boys" because they were our key labour force. The ploughing was a slow tedious process but I must say it was a remarkable sight. I loved watching the main driver chatting and calling to his animals. At the end of the furrow you would hear a great cracking of the long ox-hide whip and more shouted instructions. Like magic the leading pair of oxen would start to turn and carry on working down the return furrow. My father watched it all avidly.'

'What did your mother think of Africa?' I could believe that Granny's father enjoyed his visit but I was unable to imagine Granny's mother 'as happy as a sandboy' fitting into the primitive lifestyle. 'Was she able to cope without the comforts?'

'Oh yes. She knew we had no inside loos and that sort of thing. I once had a friend come out called Yoskyl who was very shocked by the lack of water sanitation. She didn't stay long.'

As I recall this part of the conversation Granny suddenly makes me feel guilty that I had moaned about the loos that didn't flush at Spring Grange. I am Yoskyl II.

'My most vivid memory of their visit was hearing my father flapping at the bats in his bedroom with his towel,' Granny had continued. '"Get them out!" mother screeched! She was tucked up in her mosquito net, too frightened to move. Gerald and I laughed so much at my father chasing the swooping creatures.'

I laughed and Granny cackled loudly after me.

'Did Gerald's parents ever visit?'

'No. They didn't write much either. It hurt him.'

'Did he tell you that?'

'No, he never complained. His aunt Mildred came out though. Mildred's daughter, Jean Follett, had just recovered from appendicitis when she came to stay. Mildred kept on banging on, "Had it not been for Christian Science I don't think Jean would be alive today." Gerald and I thought it was a most comfortable faith. If you had any kind of malady that was cured, Christian Science had done the trick. I was very fond of Mildred but I did find the Christian Science thing maddening.'

I smiled.

'When Gerald took Mildred out for a walk in the bush,' Granny continued, 'she followed him literally step by step. He stopped, turned round and looked at her. She was hunched over and furiously clutching her knobbed stick, her eyes rooted to the ground!' Granny described. '"Why are you walking in my footsteps Milly?" Gerald asked.

"I'm terrified of being bitten by a snake," she replied.

And Gerald said, "But you're a Christian Scientist. If you're bitten you have your faith!"' Granny hooted with laughter.

'I'm glad someone from Gerald's family came out. It must have meant a lot to him.'

'Oh it did. He was especially thrilled that my father took such an interest. We had some terrible luck while they stayed but my father still supported our venture.'

April 1928

The tobacco expert from Salisbury was visiting the farm. He

told Gerald that the tobacco crop was 'very good indeed'. Gerald was thrilled that after months of experimenting he was finally getting the hang of growing tobacco. From little seedlings, shaded and watered daily in carefully prepared, sterilised soil, they had grown into a magnificent tall crop. Half the battle of growing a decent crop was in the preparation and the other half was the weather which, so far, had not let them down. When the tobacco was planted out in the ploughed fields they had had a good deal of rain to help them grow. Now, it was April and the crop, which Margaret said looked delicious like spinach, was almost ripe. Gerald was about to pick the leaves off and start the curing process – the tobacco had to dry out at exactly the right temperature in the barns.

'Once the tobacco is cured, will it go all the way to the market at Salisbury?' Father asked.

'Yes, and I am hopeful that it will sell at a substantial profit. Prices are quite promising at the moment.'

'Well, you ought to make a good sum of money from the crop. I'm sure it will do very well,' Father predicted as he put his hand on his son-in-law's shoulder. 'Well done indeed.'

Margaret and her parents were sitting peacefully on the verandah when the storm broke. Margaret saw Gerald running in from the fields. 'Is Anne with you?' he shouted. Anne had been with Gerald but had wandered off, saying she was going to find Granny.

'No, I thought she was with you,' Margaret shouted back. Gerald approached the verandah and shepherded her and Margaret's parents inside.

Hailstones as large as marbles pelted down. 'Where's Anne?' Margaret panicked. 'She's never around when you want her.'

Anne finally joined them, great puddles of water spreading round her feet. Margaret pulled Anne towards her, 'Where have you been?' she sighed with relief. Anne told her she had been watching the boys milking the cattle. Margaret asked Elardie to fetch her a towel.

They sat huddled together until the storm subsided. Margaret dried Anne and gave her a new dress to put on. It was a long half hour during which time they played cards, but Gerald could not concentrate, constantly keeping an eye out at the sky, hoping the storm would go as quickly as it had come.

Gerald stood speechless as he looked at the tobacco plants all torn to ribbons. What had been a handsome crop was reduced to shreds. There was nothing left to salvage. It was a mess. The fields looked as if a battle had been fought on them, the dead and wounded plants strewn over each other haphazardly. He closed his eyes tightly and prayed that when he opened them he would see another picture. But who was he fooling? This kind of thing happened all the time. Yet he had not believed it would happen to him. Why was life so cruel? He felt sick as he turned to Margaret. She burst into tears. He put his arms around her but all Gerald could muster to comfort her this time was, 'At least the crop is insured.' But the insurance money will be pitiful, giving us a tiny sum compared to what we would have made at Salisbury, he thought.

They walked back to the house to face her parents. It wasn't his fault. The weather had dealt him, and many other farmers, a cruel blow. So why did he feel such a failure?

'That was awful but no one's fault. But we were so hard-up you see, we had no money and had been relying on that tobacco to do well. It was our livelihood.'

'How depressing.'

'Yes, very depressing. Still, that was life. After the tobacco disaster we realised that selling cream and maize was the "safe wicket" on the farm. The cows gave us wonderful milk and cream which we sold at Bulawayo.'

'Going back to your parents, it must have been hard saying goodbye?'

'No, they were ready to go home.'

'But you must have been very weepy?'

'I probably was, I don't remember.'

Granny crossed her legs and arms tightly in front of her. I suddenly wanted to give her a hug. She probably wanted to cry at the memories but was desperately trying not to.

'Oh, darling,' she said as I kissed her. She gave me a big kiss in return. 'Father gave me a gift when he left,' she started again.

Margaret's father slipped an envelope into her hand. He shook his head as if to say, 'I don't want you to open it until I'm gone.' He then turned to Gerald, saying he wanted to back their loss with a cheque for £3000 to help them recover from the hail storm. Gerald felt embarrassed taking the money, but on the other hand he knew that they could not survive without it. 'We are determined to make money out here somehow,' Gerald vowed to her parents. 'We will make it a success.'

Alone, Margaret opened the letter. There was a cheque for £300. 'I want you to spend this money on a trip home,' he wrote. 'My little gypsy, come and see us soon.' Margaret felt tears in her eyes. He had not called her his little gypsy since she was little. It was her nickname because her skin tanned so easily. 'Love, Daddy.'

'That's right, he did,' Granny recollected. 'And I did have a lovely time at home in 1929. I can remember exactly what Anne said when we returned to M'Coben after our holiday. She turned to Gerald and said, "You know castles are much nicer, this is really rather a poor little house, why can't we have a castle?"'

'What a madam!' I laughed.

'Yes, a real madam!' Granny echoed with laughter.

I tried to steer Granny back to her parents' parting at M'Coben. 'I would have been very upset saying goodbye to my parents. I can remember feeling tearful when Mum and Dad dropped me off at Bristol University, and I was only an hour and a half's drive away. I remember Mum turning her back on me because she was afraid to show she was crying. She knew how unwell I was and was terrified of how I was going to cope on my own. I had spent almost a whole year at home by then so I knew I was going to be homesick and scared.'

'Oh darling.'

'They left me in my dingy room to unpack and the moment they'd gone I started to put their photographs on the wall. Dad and Mum at their wedding anniversary, Mum and I together. Just from that experience, I can imagine how you felt saying goodbye to your parents.'

'My father realised I missed all the things at home, one could say the "luxuries of civilised living". I think he wisely guessed that once I went home for a holiday, I would settle down and be a better colonial's wife.'

'If it had been your choice would you have gone back to England?'

'I did hanker after the past. I missed my family and friends dreadfully. I missed the weddings at home. I was sad that Anne could not be Barty's bridesmaid. You see, Barty was her godfather. Mother always sent me family photographs but nothing matches up to being there.'

'Did you really want to be in England?' I asked again.

'No, I was determined to make it work and support Gerald,' she says firmly. 'And I was ever so happy. We made M'Coben a wonderful home and I had everything I wanted. I used to love riding before breakfast and the sunsets were magical. When I went back to England I missed my busy life on the farm and was always happy to get back to M'Coben. The "goodbyes" never got easier though. If anything they got harder. Saying goodbye to my father was awful because I knew it was our last parting.'

'When was this?'

'In 1929. I wanted to go home because I knew from mother's letters how unwell he was. He died on my birthday the following year. I remember receiving the dreaded cable.'

June 1930

Gerald took Margaret's hand and held it gently. 'I am here if you need me,' he promised. Margaret looked up to him, but at this moment nothing could bridge the gap between her and Gerald. She wanted him to go away. There he was, sitting in front of her, offering himself, yet nothing but her mother would do. Margaret wanted to hold and console her.

Gerald knew he was a poor substitute. He took Anne away to tell her what had happened seeing Margaret needed some time on her own. He shut the door quietly.

He was not surprised by the cable. Margaret's father had looked no more than a skeleton when they were in England, and he had had dreadful pains in his chest.

'Where's Granddad now?' a confused Anne asked. Gerald would have loved to be able to say 'in heaven' but the truth was he had no idea. 'In a safe place,' he replied, hoping not to be pressed further. Anne nodded her head, and said she wanted to see Mummy. 'Not now,' Gerald replied firmly and, at that, Anne began to cry.

Margaret's father had died, aged sixty-one, in the early hours of 26 June 1930. 26 June was Margaret's birthday. 'The cause of his death was hardening of the arteries,' the doctor confirmed. Margaret was not exactly sure what that meant but she did not care.

An hour later Gerald went back into the sitting room and found Margaret reading a letter. He sat close to her, her face was still stone cold and she did not look up. She was reading one of her father's old letters. They stood in a pile, tied with string and carefully labelled, 'Letters from Daddy'. Gerald watched her as she picked up another letter her father wrote from Egypt. He and Mother had left for Egypt in the winter, in the hopes of finding sun and restoring his health. Normally it worked.

Margaret shook her head slowly as she read the hopeful letter saying how much better he was feeling. 'He was only trying to be brave to protect me,' she muttered at last. 'When we said goodbye, I could feel every bone through his night-shirt. I knew it was our last parting.' Her father had written in his letter how much he missed Anne and Diana. Diana loved perching on Granddad's knee. Every morning she would climb on to his bed and give him a big kiss. He loved to spoil Anne too, feeding her strawberries and cream for breakfast. Margaret shut her eyes, remembering the image of him tying a napkin carefully around Anne's little neck. And how she had loved to watch him shave as a child. 'Margaret, surprise,' he smiled as he put a blob of shaving soap on to her nose. She could even hear the noise it made as he stropped his razor: plip, plop, plip, plop. She used to fiddle with his little silver sovereign case and the gold and silver coins which lay on the dressing table. She could see him handing out the pocket money, a penny a week for every year of their age. 'Cut along now,' he said, trying to shoo them out of his room to get dressed. She could even hear the familiar loud blowing of his nose as he descended the stairs to go to his study. 'La trompette de mon pere,' the French governess had called it. Margaret could picture his proud face when she had managed to swim in the river without the water wings he had brought for her from America. She smiled remembering the way he used to take out his watch at the start of a church sermon and place it in the pew in front of him. It was a blessing as the parson never preached for that long.

How she longed to see him one more time. To hear him call her, 'My little gypsy'. Margaret wished she could tell him she loved him. She could not remember the last time she had said those three words. Maybe she never had. Why was it always too late?

Gerald was thinking hard what to say. 'He died peacefully in his sleep, that is a blessing,' he said, immediately wanting to take it back. It did not seem right to say anything was a blessing. 'You cared for him,' Gerald attempted, 'as much as you could, and Mother has the family with her now.'

Just not me, Margaret wanted to say as she turned to him. She took a deep breath, 'I feel he will understand and be with us through the ups and downs of our life out here, I feel he is here, with us.'

Gerald nodded, saying his spirit would never die. 'He was as good as a real father to me too and I will miss him.'

Margaret sat down to write another letter. She had written one almost every day since the cable, some she did not send, but somehow just by writing she felt closer to home. She had reread her mother's letters over and over again.

'I am simply amazed by your bravery and the way you are carrying on, when I know what your life is like now that the one person who really matters is gone.'

Margaret told her mother that she would come home if she wanted her to. Gerald was wonderful, helping her as much as he could and Anne was like a little angel holding her hand and comforting her in her own way. So why did she feel this desperate sense of isolation?

'I sometimes wish we did not feel things so deeply, and yet life without deep emotions, both sad and happy, would be colourless indeed.'

Anne rested her head against her shoulder.

'Granddad will be a living memory to my Anne.'

'It was hard being so far away,' Granny admitted. 'The only thing that kept me going was the news that Mother and sister, Helen, were going to come out and stay. You see, I was pregnant again.'

CHAPTER TWENTY-TWO

February 2000

I'm sitting in a place called, 'Afrinet Surfing,' in Bulawayo, emailing an old college friend, Sophie.

'My feet are too sore for shopping. Helen and James are still with us which is great. I needed some young company. We've just been to a wildlife orphanage on the outskirts of Bulawayo. We came within a couple of feet of a cheetah, it rolled on its back for us like a tame cat. The highlight though was seeing a lion which roared and then proceeded to piss backwards on a Japanese tourist and his camera.

We are staying at Spring Grange again. Before Helen and James saw Spring Grange I had told them the place was palatial. It is lovely too, but there are bugs everywhere. The cat even killed a bird in my room in the middle of the night. I could hear it munching behind the curtain. They were all teasing me at breakfast for making such a fuss about it. James asked if I needed counselling. He is just as bad though. I caught him showering in his Birkenstocks because he was scared of the spiders.

I really miss the mini bar and the hot showers at Macalister's. However, I don't miss the other guests. If I thought that there might be a hint of any holiday romance, I think I was wrong. We met a young man called Roger who worked for the Immigration Department in Harare. Helen, James and I decided he looked exactly like 'Monty' from the film, 'Withnail and I'. He had an enormous beer gut hanging over his trousers and a chipmunk face with sticking out teeth. "Potential husband?" Helen whispered to me. He also spouted a lot of rubbish. "You've never had one decent British Prime Minister, ever!" he spat over the table. "The NHS is in a terrible state and it's all Winston Churchill's fault!" he carried on. Diana and Mum decided to take Roger on. "What balls Roger," and "What absolute rubbish," were fired across the table like scud missiles. Helen, James and I left them to it. As we left we overheard Roger's assistants asking him why he bothered talking to the "two old grannies", when all they did was attack him. Helen, James and I think they should start their own travel programme, called the "Two Thin Ladies".

Two days ago we went to the Matopos Hills to see Rhodes' Grave. The hills are a spectacular sight – enormous great boulders perched precariously on smaller rocks. How do they remain so balanced? There was no way we could use the wheelchair there. Helen told me I had to get to the top to see the incredible views. She and James would even carry me over the difficult parts if they had to. I was really proud of myself for climbing to the top and back again – a quarter of a mile each way and the end part was quite steep. I strapped on my ankle support and also have a cunning new way of cushioning my feet without wearing socks (way too hot for socks) and getting blisters. Panty-liners. They are a perfect fit. If people had x-ray vision I would be a hilarious sight with my sanitary towels taped to the soles of my feet.

A Matabele guide called Desmond Zebra attached himself to us at the beginning and helped me up the steep parts. When we reached the top he asked us if we wanted to watch him feed the lizards. He squatted in the lee of a large boulder and started calling them to him. They came from all directions, some slim common lizards with yellow-striped bodies and some much larger blue, orange and green geckos. They scurried over the rocks and collected at his feet in a heaving mass. Some jumped up like hungry dogs to take bites from the moist mealie-meal in his fingers. A really weird sight. But the views from the top were breathtaking, hills towering on either side. Helen and I leant back to back taking it all in. It was so hot too, bright blue skies and the sun beaming on our faces.

Hels and James helped me climb down the last part. They are like two giants – Helen and I always say how strange it is that we are built on a totally different scale. Still, it's lucky she's six foot. I think Hels was amazed at how far I walked. It's been such a long time since I've been able to do anything like this. I am going to write a postcard to my doctor to tell him I made it to the top and back thanks to his multi-coloured support.

What other news: chicken legs are turning slightly pink. Am missing you. Write back as soon as you can with all your stories. How's London? How did your dinner party go? Did you knock everyone out with our chicken with lemon and ten cloves of garlic recipe?!

Big kiss, Alice x'

We are going back to M'Coben as Helen wants to see Mum's old home. 'I want to see where you come from,' she tells Mum.

Stewart, who is looking after Spring Grange while Barbara and Peter are away, says that he will take us in the truck to M'Coben. The roads are too slippery to take the car. Barbara and Peter have phoned to find out the result of the referendum. To our astonishment, and theirs, it resulted in a resounding NO, even from the Harare area where Mugabe used to be strongest. Barbara, Peter, Fred and Betty are extremely relieved. It was just as Diana had predicted, 'Everyone will be waiting with bated breath to see how Mugabe will react. He must be licking his wounds and wondering what to try next. There has hardly been any word from him since, apart from inevitably blaming the white man.'

Returning to M'Coben feels like a home-coming. Hairy Mary and Katie rush out with wagging tails along with Fred and Betty. 'Isn't it wonderful news about the referendum?' Mum says. After we have introduced Helen and James, Mum asks Fred if we can take them around the farm.

'This was the back of the house in our day,' Mum tells Helen. She points to the old kitchen where George made a cooked breakfast for Gerald and mealie-meal porridge for Margaret and the children each morning. Towards the end of 1928, Gerald had built Margaret a kitchen with a lock-up store room next to it, both separate from the house. Margaret was overjoyed, 'It is lovely and big enough to be the pantry as well, and a place where all the ironing can be done. Gerald has installed an enamel sink and I have been busy getting everything tidied up. All that remains to be done is to pull down the old tin shanty. At last! The next wish is to have a fridge!'

I can't imagine the day when I pull the wishbone and ask for a fridge or a washing machine. Maybe when I finally have my own flat. I've always been really lazy in the kitchen. When I was small I used to time my going to the loo at just the time when the washing-up was being done. I would never have got away with it in Granny's day. There were no machines which did it for you. She explained to me, 'An open fire was constantly burning in the back yard, heating water for dirty dishes, washing, and heating the metal strips to go inside the iron. Elardie washed and ironed the clothes with great care, praying no ash would fall out of the iron and mark or burn a hole through the garments. I had also been warned that all clothes, including nappies, must be ironed on both sides and inside out because maggot flies laid their eggs on the damp washing while it was hung out on the line. Hot ironing killed the eggs and prevented them from hatching into tiny maggots which would burrow into the skin and cause a boil-like sore. I made sure I was vigilant after hearing that one of the neighbour's boys had suffered as many as eighty maggots in his buttocks. I had also seen another girl with a maggot boil on her forehead. Presumably she had left her hat on the ground, the fly had laid an egg on the lining and when she put it back on the wretched thing had hatched and burrowed into her forehead. When the maggot was fully grown it had to be squeezed out.'

I tell Helen and James the maggot stories and can see them flinch just as I had when Granny told me. Helen hates creepy crawlies as much as I do and was not impressed when James was poking sticks through ticks and calling them, 'tick-kebabs'.

'How did Margaret cook?' James asks Mum.

'She had George, the cook-boy who prepared most of the meals. They had a two-burner paraffin stove and a wood-burning range. Cooking the babies' food was the biggest chore. She had to take great care sterilising our bottles and keeping all the other kitchen utensils separate. The boiled milk was placed in a deep bowl of cold water and covered with a double layer of butter muslin.'

James nods knowingly but it is another world to Helen, James and me. Granny's morning followed this pattern. She got up with the sun. She dressed the family. She checked that George had started to make the butter. One of the other house-boys took the children for an early morning walk while she went to the kitchen garden to gather the day's requirements. They ate breakfast at 8am. The morning milk arrived and she saw it through the separator. She then 'gave out the stores,' to George which was the measuring out of ingredients from the lock-up store-room. She ordered the meals for the day. She was ready for her medical session at 10am. She sewed and mended the children's clothes plus her own. She wrote her letters home.

Our mornings at home are something like this. Wake up. Have breakfast. Put the dishes in the dishwasher and throw some washing into the machine. Catch a tube to work or, in my case, have my daily fix of Johnny Vaughan on The Big

Breakfast and then turn on the computer.

Mum shows us the old site where the kitchen garden was, now completely overgrown with the old reservoir alongside, small trees sprouting through the crumbling stone wall. 'Ouch!' Diana exclaims as she trips up.

'What's that?' I ask, pointing to the engraved stone which Diana tumbled over. I lean closer towards it. It's an old gravestone with a knifed engraving, 'Michael and Elizabeth, October 1930'.

'Who are Michael and Elizabeth?' Helen asks.

'Margaret found out that she was pregnant just at the time when her father died,' I say. 'Granny said that the pregnancy always felt, "doomed". In her letters she calls it the "blessed baby".'

'Where did she have the miscarriage? Was there a hospital near here?' Helen asks.

'She was supposed to have the baby in England. She had had a large operation at King's College hospital in London to repair the damage caused by Diana's birth. She was badly torn. Her doctor had told her that she must have the baby in England. After Diana's birth it was too frightening to risk having the baby in Africa again.'

September 1930

'I won't go if you don't want me to,' Margaret said to Gerald as they were playing a game of backgammon in the evening. 'Can we afford the trip home?'

Gerald looked up from the board. 'You must go, you need better attention which you won't get here.' Gerald could pay for Margaret's journey home. His tobacco was good but the market still poor. However, they were making a small profit from milk and cream. Cream was being sold at the Bulawayo market, five pence per pint.

For the first time in four years they were just about managing to save. Gerald often cursed their luck. How could they have known that they were going out to Rhodesia almost on the eve of the Depression? He realised it had been looming for one or two years before they left, but it had burst with a vengeance when the Wall Street Stock Exchange crashed in 1929. The depression affected Rhodesia as it did everywhere else. From what he could gather from the letters home the whole world had plunged into recession – unemployment, factories closing, banks shutting their doors. Gerald reasoned that they were probably more comfortable in Rhodesia than they would have been back in England. Any dividends from their private money would have shrunk and he would not have had much of an income. But he could see a long tough stretch ahead of them. Prices were rock bottom, animals almost unsaleable and no crop seemed worth growing. Making money out of farming was going to be almost impossible. Small mercies were that they had been right to stick to raising cattle.

Margaret touched his hand. 'I will miss you.'

'I'll miss you too.'

'I want Anne and Diana to stay here with you. I cannot leave knowing you are on your own.'

'We'll talk about it,' he said.

Gerald was worried about Margaret. Her temper was constantly flaring, she was often sick and she had fainted a few times. He was relieved that Margaret's mother and sister,

Helen, were both coming out in October to look after her. The plan was for them to take her home to have the baby. Margaret was still grieving for her father's death and she needed her family around her. At times, Gerald felt inadequate. What should he do to help?

He was relieved that Margaret did appear enthusiastic about the building plans. With the money Margaret's father had given them, Gerald had employed a builder called Makalene, the children called him Macaroni, to build a large sitting room, a new bedroom for themselves with a bathroom cum dressing room next door and a small spare room beyond. Their bedroom was going to be blue and Gerald was considering a chess board floor for the sitting room. He was also planning to build a tennis court near to the house. The ground needed to be levelled and the hard surface would be made out of antheap soil.

Margaret had been into Bulawayo to buy mirrors and curtain trims, but what she was most delighted to have found was a proper chain to pull in the Haddon & Sly ladies lavatory for their new bathroom. 'Daddy was always keen we built on, I think that's why he gave us the money,' she had told him. 'He wanted to see our farm develop and grow.'

October 1930

Margaret's mother and sister Helen were staying. It was a warm day, the heat brewing before the start of the rains. The veldt was parched dry.

'Here comes the bird of ill omen,' Margaret's mother said as she saw the tall lanky herd boy walking towards the breakfast table, no doubt about to tell them bad news like he did every morning. Yesterday a cow had fallen into the river.

Today he told Gerald that another cow had fallen into the river and was too weak to climb out. Margaret was impressed by the way Gerald always took immediate control, gathering a rescue party to go out with ropes and a sling to haul the animal back up the bank.

'He's wonderful,' she told her mother, 'I don't know what I would do without him. We are so happy together. I must tell you, Anne is loving her reading and writing, though she pretends not to.'

It was a blessing that Gerald was so capable because she felt useless. She was tired, panted the whole time, had discovered an unwelcome varicose vein on her right leg and was longing to be rid of her bump. She prayed she would have a son this time. Gerald assured her he would be happy whatever the sex, but she knew he would love a boy.

As George cleared away the cups and breakfast plates, a sharp pain hit Margaret's back. She took a deep breath and held on to the edge of the table.

'You must go to bed Margaret,' Mother ordered, motioning to a worried George that she would see to her daughter. It began to rain heavily and Anne rushed inside to dry off, excited by the noise of thunder. 'Look, lightning!' she pointed with delight. 'I've just been riding Peter Pan, Mummy.' Peter Pan was her donkey.

'Lovely dar...' Margaret held herself straight. 'It hurts.'

'Bed,' Mother instructed again and Margaret did not protest this time. She lifted the covers, her heavy body sinking underneath them. Another wave of pain hit her, this time far worse. 'Mother!' she shouted, 'Mother, come quickly!'

Mother told George to fetch Gerald immediately. The wretched cow could wait. They needed to call the doctor at once. 'Am I going to lose the baby, oh dear God don't let me lose my baby,' Margaret prayed.

Margaret was surprised to see the doctor so quickly, his clothes were soaked, water dripping on the floor. His bald head, more like a large ostrich egg, was glistening from the rain. Another clap of thunder raged over them.

Helen and Gerald were outside the room. Gerald was pacing up and down. 'Dear God, please help. I'll never call your followers God Botherers again, I promise.'

Margaret clung to her mother's hand as the contractions began to increase rapidly leaving little time to breathe. She cried out, 'Is it too late, what's happening?'

The doctor told Margaret's mother to give her some anaesthetic. Margaret felt the pad covering her nose and part of her forehead, its fumes making her sleepy. She looked up to her mother holding the pad, 'Mother,' she said, 'is it going to be all right?' She did not have the strength to say any more. She could vaguely hear the doctor asking for some boiling water. Elardie rushed off, terrified by the sight of blood. He returned with a kettle and rushed out again.

'What's wrong with this kettle?' the doctor cursed as he lifted the lid. It was so furred up the water would not pour properly.

'I'm going to lose my child aren't I?' Margaret said. Mother wanted to leave the room, she was sure the baby would not survive and she did not want to be the one who had to tell Margaret.

Late afternoon

'You are carrying twins,' the doctor said as he delivered the first baby. 'It's a boy.'

Gerald wants to call our son Michael or Richard. I like Michael. He will stay alive for Gerald. Margaret began to cry.

The boy was tiny. Helen took him to the kitchen and held him in the oven to keep him warm. Fifteen minutes later the girl, Elizabeth, was born and she joined the little boy, Helen carefully holding them both in the oven.

'How is Margaret?' Gerald frantically asked, at last being able to talk to someone. 'How is she?'

'She's haemorrhaged very badly,' Mother told him. The sight of the blood soaking the bed was too much and she had had to leave.

Helen came out of the kitchen, her head down, holding two small bundles.

There was a painful moment of understanding.

Late that evening, Gerald wearily pulled on his boots. With one small bundle in each arm he stepped outside into the darkness. He had to find somewhere to bury the babies and the only place he could think of was the kitchen garden. The soil was soft and deep. He did not have the strength to walk up the kopje and he could not endure asking someone to help him. He had to do this on his own.

He took a spade from the worker's shed and began to dig vigorously. He carefully laid the two babies next to each other. He looked at the boy and gently touched his face. They will have a proper gravestone, engraved with their names, he decided. He stumbled across the veldt and back to the house, tears running down his face. He was too shaken to care if anyone saw him in such a state. He never wanted to talk about it. Not to anyone.

'What did Granny say about her miscarriage?' Helen asks.

'Not much, understandably. She didn't talk about it to Gerald either. Her letters show how low she felt afterwards. It's not that she brushed it under the carpet. I think she just grieved privately. Writing home was her way of letting go.'

'Yes, Gerald must have felt miserable,' Granny admitted.

'You didn't talk about it, did you?'

'Never.'

'Why not?'

'Too sad,' she stated, crossing her arms tightly. 'There was no point dwelling on it together. Gerald was too upset.'

'You never brought it up again then?'

'No, not with Gerald. I wrote to my mother afterwards and told her how sad I was, but I didn't ever talk about it like people talk today.' Granny is right. We are becoming used to a society which shoves microphones in front of us and we have to talk about our feelings all the time.

'Do you think you felt less inhibited displaying your emotions on paper?'

Granny looked blank.

'What I mean is, did you confide in your mother when you were actually with her or just in a letter? It seems you were much more formal when you were together.'

'Yes, I suppose we were,' Granny agreed.

'How old was your sister Helen at the time?'

Granny did not answer. There was a strange silence. I don't think she really heard my question.

Eventually, in a clear voice, 'We called them Michael and Elizabeth.'

She was a world away.

I had lost her.

Mum, Diana and I have just finished showing Helen and James around the farm. We took them to the waterfall where they used to play and swim. 'I took the two girls bathing in the rocky pools and it was heavenly sitting under the waterfall. Diana was in the shallow pool and would not stop eating the gravel,' Granny had said.

Diana was overjoyed to see it running, the water cascading over the lip of the rock into the pool below and swirling along the overgrown river bed downstream. We were lucky to see the waterfall today as it is the first time the stream has come down in flood for fourteen months.

We are in the sitting room enjoying some tea and muffins with Fred and Betty.

'This room was the new sitting room Gerald was building just before the miscarriage,' Mum explains. He added the bedroom next door, and later on the dining room we've just been in. Before the additions to the house my parents, Anne and Diana, all slept in one room. They needed the space for the new baby. That was the main reason for building on.'

As they continue talking I think back to one of Margaret's letters to her mother, describing how hard it was watching the building work in progress. 'I feel so depressed and poor Gerald has to put up with my rages. I sometimes can hardly bear to see the house going up when the real reason for the addition has been snatched away from me. I felt so ashamed of myself breaking down when I heard the news of Helena's baby boy – I do try so hard not to be jealous of other people's babies but it is hard to get over my disappointment and it is going to be a weary year that I have to wait before I am able to try again.'

I look over to Mum talking animatedly to Fred. He's asking her if Helen and I are the only two in the family. I can hear her saying that we have two brothers, Tom and Andrew.

Two years ago Mum told me that she had had a miscarriage between Tom and me. We were on our own in the kitchen. I was working on my first book. She was sewing. She suddenly started to talk about it.

'Why didn't you tell me before?' I exclaimed.

'I don't know,' she replied. 'I was six months pregnant. I went home as I needed my mother to look after me. She told me to lie in bed. I had a terrible haemorrhage in the middle of the night and lost the baby. I was too ill to know what was going on.' I could feel her hesitate as to whether or not to continue. She sat down opposite me. Finally she confided, 'I don't know where Mum buried the baby. I couldn't face asking. I still don't know.'

'Mum, that's awful.'

'Miscarriages are common things. It is awful, but many people go through it. It was hard losing the baby at such a late stage though. It's just like Mother's story. She lost her first son. I can understand why she never wanted to talk about losing the twins.'

'Do you think counselling would have helped?'

'Not really, but it wasn't even an option anyway. I had your father for support. I put on a brave face and carried on. That's all you can do.'

CHAPTER TWENTY-FOUR

It is our last morning at Spring Grange before we travel to Harare, but we will be coming back to stay at M'Coben for a few days before leaving for England. Dad will be coming out to join us in three days.

Helen and James left yesterday. To cheer ourselves up Mum, Diana and I went out for lunch. We each ate a large steak with chunky chips and then went shopping.

During the forthcoming week, we are going to be staying with George Bakewell, who came out to M'Coben to work on the farm as a young man.

Fred and Betty have warned us about Harare. We are staying in Borrowdale where Mugabe lives. 'When you hear the wailers, get off the road immediately and lie low,' Fred explained. The wailers are Mugabe's protection.

'A tourist was shot there the other day for not getting out of the way. Isn't that right Ducky,' Betty chipped in helpfully.

Fred has told us that if we come across the wailers we will see four motor bikes abreast, followed by two limousines with smoked glass windows so that nobody can be sure which car Mugabe occupies, and after them a procession of armoured jeeps full of men in gas masks. Each vehicle has a siren so that the wailing is loud and high. It made us begin to wonder whether we wanted to leave the security of M'Coben and enter the capital where anything could happen.

It is a long six hour drive to Harare. 'Pam, will you stop side-seat driving,' Diana snaps, 'it is most tiresome.'

'I'm sorry,' Mum dithers, before she tells Diana there's another red light coming up and presses her foot against an imaginary brake. Diana holds her tongue, as she grips the steering wheel tightly.

'Mind the pot-hole!' Mum yelps, unable to help herself. I do not dare look at Diana this time. Never mind about the wailers, it's frightening enough in this car.

Finally we arrive late afternoon, hot and bothered and strangely disappointed that we didn't come across the wailers. George greets us and immediately looks at Mum with disappointment. 'Pamela,' he pulls a disgruntled face, 'you used to be blonde.'

Mum apologises, patting her brown-with-strands-of-grey hair self-consciously.

George tells us that later on he is taking us over to his daughter Charlotte's house for supper. We are going to meet Tony Combe's son, John. 'It's a surprise,' George says. 'John doesn't know you're here.'

Charlotte whispers to Mum and Diana, 'I have told John that someone special is coming for supper tonight, but I haven't told him who.'

'Who can I pretend to be then?' Diana suggests.

John introduces himself to us, shaking our hands.

'Diana Barry,' she smiles.

'Good God,' he explodes and then dives forward to hug her.

Tony Combe was a close family friend of Margaret and Gerald's. He had served in the Royal Navy and then emigrated to Rhodesia in the early twenties. He had a ranch near Hartley, not far from what is now the Hwange game reserve. 'For

Tony, farming was always a 'secondary occupation,' Granny had explained.

Tony and Gerald both loved fishing and shooting. Once a year, they used to go for a fortnight on the Zambezi in a boat Tony hired from Katambora.

'Tony was a devastatingly good looking man, well over six foot, with dark hair, broad shoulders and an outrageously loud laugh,' Granny had described, going into a roar of laughter herself.

Margaret's letters often mention him.

'Did I ever tell you Tony Combe paid us a hurried visit on his way up to his farm. He had to rush off again after an early tea and in his rush he forgot his hat. I had to send this on and heard from him in reply, that he got home to find half his crop eaten by army-worm (caterpillars) and his dog dying of dysentery. It was nice to see him again. I do wish he was one of our neighbours.'

'We have all come up here to stay with Tony Combe for the weekend and it is great fun. The house here is a killing derelict affair, and very much eaten by white ants.

Tony and Gerald are going off on a big game shooting expedition and wanted to have a really good talk about it. I think the shooting trip will be splendid.'

Tony's fateful shooting expedition happened soon after the birth of Granny's third child, Patricia on 22 July 1932. 'Gerald was supposed to go with Tony but he wanted to stay with me. He said that the trip was too close to the birth,'

Granny told me. 'Looking back, I realise how lucky it was that he didn't go.'

Gerald had written home after Patricia was born, saying he had never seen Margaret looking so well and happy. Margaret's letters also shine at this time. 'My boys had taken great pride in getting everything polished up in honour of my homecoming. I was touched by such a welcome and felt an overwhelming sense of pride and happiness to be back with Gerald and the children. I sank down into our heavenly bed, and slept that night the sleep of a tired but very happy woman.'

Over supper we talk about John's father's accident. 'Tony would have taken with him four or five bearers to carry all the provisions and camping equipment, and to build and dismantle each camp,' John tells us. 'Possibly one or two expert Matabele trackers to follow and interpret spoor, and the cook-boy, Chimwara. How did Margaret tell the story?'

I am in the middle of telling him when he stops me in my tracks.

'My father didn't say it quite like that,' he smiles. 'Margaret tells it in the polite way. This is more-or-less what happened.'

August 1932 – in the veldt, miles from anywhere
It was a golden rule NEVER to follow a wounded big cat or any other big game into the bush. Tony had to make a quick decision. He could not allow the wounded lion to die a slow and painful death. With the tracker following the spoor, Tony crept through the bush.

He stopped for a moment as they had lost the trail. In this

split second the lion leapt at him from behind with a ferocious roar. The gun was knocked out of his hands and flew to the ground. All Tony could see were eyes, teeth and claws as he heard the gnashing sound of the lion chewing his leg and starting on the other. Tony screamed for help. No one was to be seen. His African companions had fled. Tony stretched for the gun but it was out of reach. Instead he threw his hand into the lion's mouth and grabbed its tongue.

Tony screamed again as he looked away, unable to watch. He looked up to the sky. 'Chimwara!' he shouted. Chimwara had climbed up a tree. 'Get your bloody arse down and help.'

He trembled as he clambered down.

'Pick up the gun. The gun. Pick it up,' Tony raged.

Chimwara scrambled along the ground to retrieve the weapon. He held the gun to him just as Tony was instructing. His arm was wobbling like a drunkard.

'Shoot the bloody thing,' Tony wailed. He could see the gun waving all over the place. 'Just don't shoot me,' he added.

Chimwara aimed and pulled the trigger.

After the gunshot

Chimwara rushed back with the other boys. There were shocked gasps as they looked at Tony, a mess of blood and mangled limbs. The dead lion was still lying on top of him. Chimwara, now confident, took charge, binding the legs and arms as best he could. The boys helped him, using mud in the wounds and wrapping them in leaves tied up in place with bark twine. Desperately, they carried Tony through the veldt on a machila[1], stopping for breaks and feeding Tony tea.

---

[1] A hammock made out of woven branches, poles and grass

Six days later

Slumped in the shade under a tree by the side of the road, they waited. And they waited. Chimwara looked down to Tony. His hair was now white and his skin a muddy dark blood-stained colour. He was certain they would not be able to save what was left of him. Tony groaned as he asked for some more tea. Chimwara leapt to his feet when he heard the sound of an engine in the distance. He jumped up and down, waving his arms frantically as a mail lorry approached. A message was sent to a doctor at the far off bush station.

The doctor travelled back to Tony and shuddered at the sight of his gangrenous leg and his other poisoned leg and arm. He gave him a shot of morphine before taking him to Livingstone Hospital.

One leg was amputated immediately. His other leg and arm, although badly mauled, were saved.

'Margaret and Gerald visited Tony in hospital six weeks later,' I tell John. 'They were shocked at his emaciated figure, he had shrunk to nothing but skin and bone and he no longer had his dark hair. I don't think anything could have prepared them for their visit. Whatever they talked about, he would somehow manage to bring the conversation back to the attack again. Granny said something like, "He broke into a diatribe about the ferocity of the lion's eyes, its teeth, its claws, then clutching at the strap handle above the bed he tried to demonstrate to Gerald the mode of its attack. After a minute or two he sank back into the pillows and all I could do was stroke his unwounded hand."'

'It was hard for someone who loved physical sport to lead

a more quiet life,' Mum says.

I can definitely relate to that, I think.

'I will always remember watching Tony swim. He undressed, whipped off his tin leg, hooked it by the side of the pool and jumped in. Just like that.'

'He was a great ladies man too,' Diana adds. 'In his single days I remember him bringing a girl with a lisp to M'Coben. Mother meanly put them in the furthest rooms apart she could, and every night the whole household could hear the sound of Tony creaking along the back verandah to his lady's bed.'

'Tell me more stories,' John asks as our wine glasses are refilled.

CHAPTER TWENTY-FIVE

We are leaving Harare today and heading for Kariba airport. We are going to spend three days at Bumi Hills, a twenty-five minute plane journey over Lake Kariba. The atmosphere in the car is significantly calmer. Dad is driving. When we collected him from the airport two days ago we spotted him immediately – a tall man with a pallid complexion, wearing a thick green jumper and a navy scarf. He tells me the scarf will be useful for the evening game drives.

I'm looking forward to flying today. I tell everyone in the car that there is something romantic about small planes and sitting right behind the pilot. I want to tie a scarf over my head and wear dark Audrey Hepburn shades. I ignore Mum's story about the Dutchman who fell out of the plane because the door had not been shut properly.

After a long sticky drive we arrive at Kariba airport, a tiny building in the middle of nowhere. To my surprise, we are the only people here so there are no queues. It's hard to believe we are at an airport. It's strangely peaceful in comparison to the normal chaos of airports. I fan myself with my book as we wait for our pilot to come and meet us. The heat and dust are stifling. Eventually a young man called Graham introduces himself and tells us that there is no threat of a storm and that he's ready to go.

'Granny told me that the first passenger air-trips started in 1931,' I say as we buy a few drinks from the airport shop. 'It will take about eight days to get to England from here and will cost £80 – which is less than the first class fare on the Union Castle. It is expensive but it brings a quick trip to England within reach. You will see the Barry family popping home by air with their little grip sacks and heavy luggage trailing home by sea after them before very long – won't that be thrilling!'

'But she never did fly home,' Diana says. 'It was too expensive. In fact, I think she's only been on a plane once or twice.'

Margaret and Gerald were hardly able to pay for an airfare in 1931. Late November of that year Margaret wrote, 'I feel the only benefit of living out here is the cheapness of living – that, one certainly does get – but Gerald and I cannot help regretting now having spent any money on farming. Living is cheap, farming is not.'

They had to strive for every penny they earned. From the early days of her marriage, Margaret had kept a detailed house-keeping book, accounting for every single expense, right down to how much the eggs, Bovril and rashers of bacon cost them each month. Like any other African farmer they had to contend with the many droughts and fears of foot and mouth restrictions. However, the most crippling setback in the early 1930s, which put paid to any profit they were making, was having to pay back, (after he had died,) the loan of £3000 that Granny's father had given them. Granny eventually confessed to me that they had never understood that it was a loan so the news must have come as a double shock when she was lonely and crippled with grief for her father. 'My brother needed the money because he was faced with heavy death duties,' she had explained.

'Didn't he realise you had no money? Didn't you say anything?'

'No, we didn't complain. Gerald's father couldn't help us so we raised a local loan and paid interest on it.'

In 1931 they started planning money-making schemes. They turned a grading shed into a shop and sold clothes, blankets, materials and food to the Africans. The women were the worst shoppers, pulling every item off the shelf, chattering and bargaining and then deciding to buy nothing. However, this did tide them over a hard financial period. Margaret also started organising jumble sales, selling her aged stockings and socks which she found 'went like hotcakes'. But selling a few old stockings and socks was never going to buy them the dream of flying home.

We are nearly there as Graham takes the plane down low and zooms noisily over the airstrip. Parties of impala, waterbuck, zebra and a few elephants are thrown into a frenzied stampede.

The moment we arrive at the hotel we are told the game drive starts in ten minutes. Getting to our rooms is like an obstacle course. There are too many steps. I am going to have to be organised. I must not leave anything in my room. I am sharing with Diana. I've been worried about this part of the holiday for weeks now. I wish I had my own room.

We share the drive with another couple, both kitted from head to toe in brand new safari outfits, everything khaki coloured. The husband looks as though he is modelling himself on Indiana Jones. Dad is in his old beige raincoat and woolly scarf.

Our guide, Rodgers, tells us that we have picked the right time to go on holiday – one of the best times to see the animals is now, the rainy season. The bush is tall and green and the animals are well fed. This has been one of the wettest rainy seasons and for the first time in something like fifteen years they have had to open the flood gates from the Kariba Dam. We are told that the lake has been rising 3cm a day due to all the rain. Mozambique has suffered the most appalling floods, 'the worst in living memory,'[1] leaving hundreds dead and around 1.25 million homeless. Rivers across the region burst their banks as the Cyclone Eline swept in, crashing down yet more rain on lands already waterlogged by heavy storms. Rodgers also tells us about the pregnant woman in Mozambique who scrambled up a tree, clinging to safety above Mozambique's floodwaters. I later learn her name was Sofia Pedro. The rising floodwaters had forced her out of her home. A South African military helicopter came to the rescue that day, and was told by those who had taken refuge in the tree that Sofia was about to give birth. The child was born two minutes later. The pilot flew back to a base camp and picked up a medic who cut the umbilical cord and helped as Sofia was winched to safety.[2]

We see crocodiles, impala, elephants, hippos, we are even lucky enough to watch a pair of courting lions by the airport runway.

'Where are the damn animals hey?' the khaki husband bellows.

'We should have come in the rainy season,' his mousy-haired wife complains.

'It is the rainy season,' Rodgers explains patiently for the second time.

We're praying we don't have to share the Land Rover with them again.

---

[1] BBC News, Monday 6 March 2000 [2] BBC News, Thursday 2 March 2000

Over the next two days I realise there was no need to worry about the sharing of rooms. Diana and I enjoy our conversations at the end of the day, sitting out on the balcony and watching the elephants.

'I haven't felt comfortable about the 'servant' thing,' I tell Diana. When we stayed with George in Harare, I had asked him if he could tell me where an ashtray was. 'Frank, get the girl an ashtray,' he shouted gruffly. 'I can get it, tell me where one is,' I had said, shrinking with embarrassment and shame as Frank came into the room and handed me one. When I asked George if he had a pen, he shouted to Frank again.

'Look, I can get it. Please don't bother Frank.'

'That's what he's there for,' George huffed.

'He's not your bloody slave,' I had muttered under my breath. I walked out of the room to find my own pen.

'I know some people do treat their workers appallingly,' Diana concedes, 'but if Frank was treated badly he wouldn't stay with George. George does a lot for him and pays for the education of Frank's child. Didn't you see Frank's pride in the house when he first showed us around?'

I nod half-heartedly. I've talked to Dad about this too. He told me it's normal to feel this way, but that I must understand what it was like in Granny's day. 'It was natural for Granny to have servants, as natural as it is for you not to have them,' he explained. 'My mother, as a young married woman in London in 1930, had six living-in servants.' Dad smiled wryly as he went on, 'She didn't know what to do with them, but everybody else in her life-style had them, so she thought she'd better have them too. Don't get hung up by the idea that domestic service is demeaning to the servant, that's boring,' he insisted. 'The master-servant relationship does carry its risk of corruption and unkindness, the failure to treat another human being with dignity. But,' he paused carefully, 'there is no need for it to be so. Granny would never have behaved in such a way. Nor would Fred and Betty, Peter and Barbara or the Piercys. In Africa in the 1930s the African servants of Margaret and Gerald were, on the whole, wonderfully happy and content; possibly much more so than they might have been if they had not been there.'

'You have to remember that your mother and I were brought up like this,' Diana says. 'Our house-boys were like family to us. We were devoted to all of them; Elardie, George, Raden. I think Raden was a special favourite.'

Raden had come to M'Coben when Patricia was little, having previously worked for one of the neighbours. Margaret made him a new M'Coben uniform consisting of trousers and a white shirt, covered by a long white apron and a round white pillbox hat. He also owned a diamond-patterned tank top of which he was especially fond.

'Patricia loved to tickle and poke the bump, the size of a currant bun, which he had on the back of his head. She could twist him round her little finger. It was rather a peculiar bump,' Diana reflects. 'I was old enough to remember the times when we went back to England to stay with Granny,' she continues. 'They had a cook called Mrs Davies, a head parlour-maid and a chauffeur who lived at Homington.' Homington was where Granny's mother moved after the death of her husband. It is close to Longford.

'When I was sent back to England I lived with the Pethericks. That was mother's eldest sister Jeane's family,'

Diana explains. 'They lived in Winchester, St Cross. Jeane had a cook and a nanny and so it went on. I knew nothing else. We were always taught to be considerate and polite to our staff and they did become great friends.'

Margaret's first child, Anne, was sent back to England in 1934 when she was ten years old. Diana went back to England in March 1936. She was eight. It was the English colonial tradition for children to be sent 'home' to school where they were to be cared for by relatives. Margaret's letters express how much she hated being parted from them. 'Diana is such a companion for me and I really do not feel, at present, as though I can lose another daughter.'

When Jeane offered to look after Diana Margaret tried to reconcile herself to the belief that she was doing it for the child's own good and she must not think of herself. Jeane had five children and the youngest, Jenefer, was Diana's age. They would be perfect companions. 'It would not be right to put our own selfish view between her and the tremendous happiness and advantages that life will bring to her. I can hardly bear to think of losing her, but I know there will be peace of mind for us, which will compensate for her loss. For I know I should have worried with her at the Bulawayo school, for fear that she would pick up undesirable habits. Diana is so adaptable and does pick up accents and habits very easily, but in Jeane's life there is really nothing undesirable that she can pick up.'

Diana and I laugh as we recall the letter.

'To begin with I was perceived as a little savage.' Diana lights a cigarette. 'I wasn't used to the formality and rigidity of Jeane's household. It was alien to me. I was told off by Eliza, the nanny, who had worked at Longford, for not holding my spoon properly. I asked her why she hadn't told me before and she said, "but Diana, there were so many things to tell you."'

I smile. 'Did you get told off a lot?'

'It was a fairly stormy household but I was expected to be unaware of any trouble. It was brushed firmly under the carpet. If Jenefer or I showed any signs of grumpiness or, heaven forbid, rudeness,' Diana stresses, 'Eliza declared sorrowfully that we were out of sorts and must have a little grey powder that night.'

'What's that?'

'A mild laxative, meant to cure most ills,' she says, tongue-in-cheek, 'including ill-bred expressions of undesirable emotions such as anger.'

'I think that's shocking, tranquillising you. You should be able to sulk occasionally. It's only normal!'

'I think it's hilarious. The concept was that well brought up people should be courteous at all times. If a child displayed any kind of emotion we were considered a bit liverish and a mild laxative would do the trick. It did us no physical harm and had no tranquillising properties at all. We were never given the powder in Africa. I should think the absence of any laxative programme in the Barry family was all part of the "little savage" image!'

'Did you like Jeane?'

'I liked her but I don't remember her tucking me up in bed or kissing me goodnight. Every morning Jenefer and I had to go into her bedroom at eight o'clock, once we were dressed. Jenefer and I sat sideways on the edge of the bed, each day learning another sentence from the Collect for the week. I remember Aunt Jeane always being propped up against the pillows, wearing a pink hairnet and eating dried prunes.'

'What is it with that generation and constipation?' I exclaim. 'Every time Granny comes to stay she and Mum have to make weekly visits to Boots to buy Senokot. One time the girl behind the prescription desk said to Granny, "You shouldn't take more than one or two tablets a day." Granny shuffled on her stick and pronounced, "I've never heard such nonsense. I take ten pills every single day and have done so for over fifty years. I'm now ninety-six so it can't have done me much harm. Give me two packets."'

Diana nods knowingly. 'Gerald was the same. In one of his war diaries there is an account about the breaking of one of the sieges of Tobruk. The day came when the British army had to break out of the stronghold in the face of enemy fire. Really dangerous stuff, walking through the sand, praying not to stray into a minefield. Father doesn't go into any of this. He was entirely preoccupied with the fact that he had not done his daily poo and there was nowhere to do it in private – no bushes in the desert, no thunderboxes.' Diana lights another cigarette. It was probably his way of avoiding telling how frightened he was. He would have considered it shameful to admit to fear.' She sits back in the chair as if thinking about what she has just said. 'I don't know actually. I wish he was alive so I could ask him.'

'What was it really like though being away from home?' I ask her. 'Margaret wrote in her letters that you were counting the days before leaving, that you were thrilled by the prospect. Is that true?'

'I think I was quite excited. Anne was in England and she was a goddess to me. She was everything I wasn't – pretty, thin, brave and funny and she could draw like an angel. She had it all going for her. She teased me unmercifully, but I adored her. I felt quite lost without her. To be truthful, I was bored on the farm. I would never have dared articulate this but life was pretty monotonous. I had no friends my age and Patricia and Gill were like twins. I was the odd one out.' Gill was Granny's fourth child, born in January, 1934. 'I confess to being disappointed that she was not a boy, but she is such a lovely baby that the disappointment was short-lived,' Margaret wrote.

'I had nothing to stretch my imagination. My parents knew I was clever so it probably was the best thing for me,' she decides.

'Did you cry leaving? Would that have been allowed?'

'Oh yes, but I don't think I did cry. The night before I left I was allowed to stay up for grown-up supper. We had home-made mulberry ice-cream and although I was a greedy girl I couldn't eat any of it. On the way to the station the next day we had to be towed through black vlei by a team of oxen. It was quite exciting but it was then that a reservoir of unshed tears filled up deep inside. It's remained ever since. It overflows unexpectedly sometimes,' she giggles.

I'm not sure what to say next, but Diana makes it easy for me by continuing, 'I was luckier than most colonial children. Some didn't see their parents for years. My whole family visited me in 1937.'

'Were you still at the Pethericks, busily trying to avoid picking up undesirable habits?'

She smiles. 'Yes, becoming a little less of a savage. I was ill when they came to see me. I was diagnosed with having a "quinsy". I'm not sure what that is,' she continues when she sees my puzzled face, 'but when they came into my bedroom I couldn't stop coughing and I remember a large slimy lump, like a toad, flew out of my mouth and on to the blankets. I was always ill when my parents came back from Rhodesia. I am sure that was brought on by psychosomatic processes, perhaps a ploy to gain love and attention.'

'Were you normally healthy?'

'Yes, pretty much.'

'Did you resent Mum, Patricia or Gill for not being sent home?'

'No,' Diana says firmly, 'not at all. They were far too young.'

'What about your parents?'

'Father missed six years of my life, from the age of ten to sixteen. Not having a father was hard. I turned Gerald into an idol, but he wasn't real. I knew he loved me and I loved him. Then there was the war. Of course nothing was the same after that.' She pauses as she is thinking. 'As I grew up I had to make myself get to a level where I could love, "warts and all". My parents weren't infallible. I loved them all the same though. But then, everyone as they grow up has to go through this transition in their relationships with their parents. Mine with father had to span a bigger gap, that's all.'

'If you could have your life all over again, would you have wanted to stay in Africa?'

'No, I don't think so. I loved being with Anne and going to school with her.'

'When you describe your upbringing it is incredible to me. It was only sixty years ago but it seems like it was in Victorian times.'

'The Second World War swept these kinds of social customs away.'

'Thank God.'

'I feel lucky to have had the experience of being brought up in Rhodesia. It was so removed from the socially stereotyped environment in England. Having the two influences has made me who I am. Whatever you experience, good or bad, goes into making you the person you are.'

I agree. Even if I could hide my RA I would not now because it is a part of who I am. It shapes what I am doing here – writing, being in Africa and re-tracing Granny's steps. All the bad experiences I have been through – the surgery, the highs and lows of university life have made me really appreciate the good times. 'Does that make up for being separated from your parents?'

'Yes, I think so.'

Rodgers, the guide, lifts me down from the Land Rover. We've just been on an early morning game drive which I was determined not to miss. In fact, I could have missed it. The animals were hiding. Rodgers, hard pushed, got out of the car to show us a dung beetle.

Mum is waiting with the wheelchair. Luckily the hotel lent it to us. We left ours at M'Coben because it would have been so boring and impractical lugging it around.

I shuffle my feet and position my bottom to land in the middle of the seat. It's a relief that we are leaving today because I would not be able to get down all those steps to my bedroom. I think that's why my ankle is hurting, along with the build up of travelling. I haven't done as much in the last six years as I have done on this holiday. I can't think how I climbed up to Rhodes' Grave when I cannot even put any weight on my ankle now. It feels as if someone has savagely wrenched my foot off my leg, twisted it around, the bones scrunching and cracking, and then shoved it back on again. The support doesn't even help it.

'Are your feet up on the pedals?' Mum asks. The last thing she wants to do is run over them. That really would finish them off.

Mum takes me to the pool and lifts me out of the chair, twists me round and lowers me on to the sun-lounger in one movement. We have these kinds of manoeuvres sussed.

'Ouch, it hurts,' I groan as I lift my swollen ankle on to the sunbed. I lean back in exhaustion and close my eyes. Mum tells me she'll ask a member of staff for some ice. She comes back and holds the cold cubes gently around the ankle joint.

Dad comes to join us, still dressed in his long trousers and shirt, and his beige sun hat. He tells us he might brave it and go for a swim. I am not sure I have ever seen him in shorts and the last time I saw him swim was when I was about four. I remember his wispy brown hair, long alabaster legs and pale blue swimming trunks which came down to his knees.

'When I'm like this it still scares me,' I say to Mum as I watch a young girl running around the side of the pool.

'Of course it does, it wouldn't be normal if you didn't feel that way. Look at him,' she suddenly smiles, pointing to Dad. He is now hovering nervously by the steps of the pool, having changed into the very same blue swimming trunks.

'Go on Dad, jump in,' I shout.

He plunges forward. 'Sod it, it's cold.'

It's mid-day and Mum, Dad, Diana and I are sitting peacefully on the Kariba ferry. The ferry will take us to Milibesi, near to the Bulawayo – Falls road. Our next trip is to see the Victoria Falls.

Lake Kariba has the feel of a Mediterranean Riviera and is quite beautiful. It is spectacularly large, like an ocean, reaching to the distant horizon.

There are only ten people on the boat. Many tourists have cancelled because of threatening cyclones and the petrol shortage. Mum is relieved that the ferry is chugging along at a leisurely 7mph. 'I was dreading this part of the holiday,' she confesses. 'I still hate boats.'

'I know,' I say. 'Remember that ferry crossing to France?' Three years ago Mum, Dad and I went to Normandy. The sea was rough – the wind was force seven. 'Dad, a paper bag,' I pleaded as I saw Mum's face. The ferry lurched from one side to another and we could barely speak. Dad stood up and swayed to the sounds of cutlery and plates crashing to the floor. He staggered back, his face chalky white, weakly clutching a paper bag. Mum shook her head hopelessly. She had already thrown up in her Duty Free bag. Dad kept the paper bag for himself.

Mum laughs as I recall the story. 'As a baby I was seasick,' she tells me as we start to play cards. 'Did Granny talk to you about my birth?'

'No, never.'

'Oh,' Mum tries not to look disappointed. Seconds later, 'She must have done,' she questions again.

Gerald and Margaret at their Golden Wedding Anniversary, London 1972

M'Coben

Alice on a tour of M'Coben

The gates and fencing around M'Coben

Fred Duckworth

Betty Duckworth

Ambrose and Diana in kraal

Above, families at M'Coben   *Ambrose driving in the Toyota*

Pam and Diana walking at M'Coben

James and Helen sitting by Rhodes' grave at the Matopos Hills

Spring Grange

Barbara and Peter Hubert on the verandah at Spring Grange

Colin and Pam on Safari at Bumi Hills

Margaret and Alice discussing the book at Margaret's home in Mickleton

Margaret at Helen's wedding to James, January 2001, aged 98

Colin and Pam on Safari at Bumi Hills

Margaret and Alice discussing the book at Margaret's home in Mickleton

Margaret at Helen's wedding to James, January 2001, aged 98

'Of course she did, you believe anything, don't you,' I smile. Mum looks relieved. 'What did she say?'

'I did not know I was having twins until I was eight months pregnant. Just before they were born Gerald organised a picnic for me with Patricia, Gill and Frances.'

'Who's Frances?'

'She was the Irish nanny and governess too. She had flaming red hair and a quick temper. For some reason she didn't like Patricia, telling her she was nothing more than a "butterfly". "You'll come to nothing my girl, nothing!" she said.'

'That's terrible. How unkind.'

'Yes, very unkind, and look how wrong she was. But Frances was too good a nanny for me to sack her. She became invaluable when the twins came along. Gerald took me to the Matopos and I whispered to Patricia, "I'm having a baby. I might even be having two babies." Patricia's face lit up and she asked if she could tell Gill. I nodded and she whispered loudly into Gill's ear. "Don't be silly," was Gill's reaction! I suppose Gill must have thought I was just fat. The next day I gave birth. The labour lasted most of the day.'

November 1938, Bulawayo nursing home.
'The news has been confirmed! I am having twins and they are both alive and kicking! The doctor says they should both be strong and healthy. I am enormous. My legs are like balloons from all the pressure of staggering around with such a weight! Oh please let one of them be a boy! Gerald is very good and always says he'll be happy with either sex but I know how he LONGS for a boy.'

Gerald took the family for the picnic on the Matopos to celebrate Margaret having two babies. The drive back was intensely hot and bumpy. 'If this does not bring the babies on, I don't know what will!' Margaret said to Gerald.

Gerald smiled back. All he could think about was whether Margaret might have a boy this time. He tried to imagine what it would feel like finally being told that he had a son. 'Gerald, you have a son,' he practised to himself over and over again.

14 November

'It must have been that drive yesterday,' the doctor suggested as he watched Margaret looking at her twins. She was stroking the little girl's dark hair. Margaret looked up at the doctor with a large smile. 'I find it hard to believe they're mine. Isn't it queer that they should look so different too! I wish Gerald was here. Have you tried ringing him again?'

'I have rung a few times but he is not answering. I'm so sorry.'

'He will be disappointed. He should be here.'

Gerald telephoned the following morning to find out how Margaret was.

'Gerald!' Margaret shrieked down the telephone. 'You have a son!'

'I'll be right there.' Without hesitation he made his way to the hospital. He hadn't heard the phone when the doctor rang, 'You must be getting deaf!' Margaret had laughed loudly.

Margaret watched as Gerald gazed down at the two babies in their cot. He looked at his boy. 'Your son was born first at about seven o'clock and his little sister ten minutes later,'

Margaret told him.

Gerald looked up, embarrassed to be seen with a tear in his eye. 'Don't think badly of me,' he said, 'but I never thought I would have a son.' He took out his camera and asked the Sister whether she would do him the honour and take a picture of himself with the children. The Sister blushed immediately and took a picture of Gerald beaming with a twin on each arm. Gerald was not sure who was who. However when he looked on their backs each baby had a plaster with its weight and name so no muddle was made. Margaret thought he looked as if he was at a baby show.

'Have you decided what you are going to call them?' the Sister asked.

Gerald and Margaret looked at each other. 'We like the name Pamela,' Margaret began.

'And we always said that if we had a son we'd call him Richard,' Gerald finished off.

The Sister took the children off Gerald's arm. 'Just fancy it, I may be looking at the future Prime Minister,' she smiled as she laid Richard back in his cot.

'Where are the girls?' Margaret asked.

'Frances took them to a teashop. They've been dressing up in your clothes and high-heels,' Gerald rolled his eyes. 'Clomping around with your dresses trailing behind them. She'll bring them in later.'

'Frances,' Patricia announced loudly, 'I think it is very lucky Mummy has got two white babies instead of two black ones.'

Gill put her glass down. 'Yes, if they had been black we should have had to give them to the boys. You know,

Fwances,' Gill spoke clearly, 'Black boys are quite black, they're black all over, although I can't quite remember about this,' she said as she pointed to her teeth.

Frances looked frantically around before telling the girls it was time to go.

Women came from the kraals offering small gifts of eggs, or two small chickens to congratulate Margaret on the birth of the twins. They looked curiously at the two babies, not daring to stand too close, but Margaret was relieved that they had come at all. It was a tradition that Margaret gave a present to each mother every time a baby was born, but since she had been in Africa she had never come across a mother having twins. Mrs Mitchell told her that it was considered by the natives to be an unfortunate birth – that one or other of the infants would be cursed with the evil eye or something worse, so no chances were taken. 'They are put down like pets,' Mrs Mitchell explained. 'Neither twin is allowed to live.'

Only a month after the birth of Richard and Pamela a mother came to Margaret with her twins, two boys. The young mother's face looked delighted rather than stricken with fear at having a 'cursed' child. Margaret was touched to think that her twins might have dispelled the tradition that twins were not a normal birth.

'When the twins were a month old we all went into Bulawayo,' Granny told me. 'Gerald and I had bought the girls tricycles which we hid in the back of the truck. When we reached the spruit we found there had been a freak storm and the river was in a raging flood. We couldn't get the car across so we sent Raden on his legs to fetch help.' I could tell from Granny's animated expression that she was enjoying telling this particular story. 'Raden whipped off his pillbox hat and waded through the river, the water reaching well up to his thighs. The farm boys came running down the hill laughing and shouting with excitement. Gerald made them stand shoulder to shoulder and they made a human chain across the water. First the little girls were handed across from one boy to the next. Then the two twins were handed over like precious white bundles. Oh, it was a wonderful sight, Alice. It was the one time I deeply regretted not having a camera.'

'I wish you had taken a picture too, I would have loved to see it.'

I have looked through Granny's Africa albums. Black and white photographs with torn edges carefully pasted into now battered books, but the pictures are packed with memories for her. She keeps the albums in a window box in her bedroom. Even though she can't see them any more she would hate to be parted from them.

'Who carried you across, Granny?' I asked her. 'Gerald?'

'Of course Gerald. It was poor Frances who had no knight in shining white armour. She paddled across on her own and got very wet!' Granny laughed wickedly.

I laughed with her. 'Raden was special wasn't he? He loved your children as if they were his own.'

'Yes, he did. I was tearful watching him so concerned to get the twins safely to the other side. He was beside himself when little Pam was so ill.'

11 January 1939. Children's hospital, Bulawayo.
'Darling mother

Just a scribble to tell you our darling Pamela is desperately ill and Gerald and I are just holding on as tight as we can. I never thought she would last even until now but she is making a brave struggle.'

Pamela was sick with enteritis. Gerald had immediately arranged for her to see one of the best children's doctors in Bulawayo. The doctor had diagnosed the problem as over-feeding, prescribing a food called Eledon to help with the severe tummy upsets. However, Pam could not take it and had been violently sick. Her condition was critical.

Margaret held the torch and looked down into Pam's cot. She expected her baby to die in the night.

Gerald came to see Margaret the following morning. He realised no recovery was possible and promised to stay overnight with her at the hospital.

'She must be christened,' the Sister told Gerald and Margaret.

Margaret was too weak to say anything. Gerald stood up and said he would see to it.

He had no idea whether he would be able to find anyone in time, Pam had only hours, perhaps minutes to live. One of the fathers of a little boy in the hospital stopped Gerald to ask how Pam was. Gerald ran on without stopping and called back, 'not good.'

'At least it's not the boy,' Gerald heard.

Gerald stopped in his tracks and turned round to face him.

'What did you say?'

'At least it's not the boy,' he repeated tentatively.

Gerald shot him a warning look. 'How dare you talk like that. All my children are dear to me.' He bolted down the stairs and out of the hospital, heading towards Archdeacon Gibbs' house.

Archdeacon Gibbs took Pamela into his arms. She was no more than a small bundle of bones. 'Dear God,' Margaret started to pray, 'I know we've always wanted a boy but little Pamela means everything to us too. Please don't take her away.'

The Sister carefully altered Pam's food, feeding her hourly albumen water with brandy and glucose in between. 'She is looking better,' she reported, smiling warmly at Gerald. 'Constitutionally Pam is very strong. Even at her worst her pulse has remained steady, however weak. It's a miracle she's still here,' she looked down at the baby, shaking her head incredulously.

Gerald did not want to raise his hopes too much as they were by no means out of danger yet. However, even a non-believer like himself had to agree that since Pam had been christened she had taken a different turn.

After eight weeks in hospital
'Welcome home Inkosikazi,' George, Elardie and Raden greeted Margaret in unison. They were in their best clothes. Raden had put on his diamond-patterned tank top especially for the homecoming occasion. He looked at Pam, a tiny bundle who only weighed seven pounds. He leaned forward to kiss Pam's

small hand and then looked up, scared to have offended. Margaret touched Raden's arm, 'Thank you,' she said.

Two weeks after Pam had arrived home, Margaret asked Raden whether he would like to continue as chef, helping George in the kitchen, or look after the twins. He thought for a moment and then his face cracked into a broad smile. 'Babies please.'

'I don't think I would have got through this without Richard,' Margaret told Gerald that evening in bed. 'He's kept me sane.'

Gerald nodded. Losing a child had to be a parent's worse nightmare. He wasn't sure he could do it again, he thought as he lay close to Margaret. Well, he didn't have to. Pam continued to get better from day to day, gaining weight and strength. She had come through the battle on a diet of egg-white. She was a miracle baby.

The ferry continues to chug on as if time has no meaning whatsoever. 'You were a miracle baby,' I declare loudly. 'Saved by egg-white and alcohol.'

'Sounds about right,' Mum says. 'Stop teasing.'

The girl in charge tells us that we are welcome to have a swim. It's hot now and there is nothing more I'd like than to strip off and dive into the water. However, I can't. My ankle is still causing a lot of pain. One of the helpers on the boat had to lift me from the car on to a chair and carry me up the steps. Despite the constant rest and being pushed around in a wheel-chair the ankle is no better. When I feel like this all the bad days come flooding back. However, I do know that the pain will eventually shift, a luxury I never had before.

Dad decides not to swim because he fears crocodiles might have followed the ferry, feeding off the scraps thrown overboard. Mum and Diana are saying that they daren't swim in case they catch bilharzia. Instead we play some more cards. What a wild party we are.

A few hours later Mum turns to me. 'I was thinking about my birth,' she starts, 'and I always feel touched by my father saying that all his children were dear to him, not only his boy.' She puts the cards back in the box. 'It's strange hearing that story. It's hard to believe it was me. I suppose it was a miracle I lived.' She looks at me with a smile, 'And just think, if I hadn't lived you wouldn't have been born.'

'Not such a bad thing,' I say.

'Stop it, Alice. Nor would we be sitting on a ferry on Lake Kariba, drinking our vodkas and tonics peacefully.'

Just as she says that I hear a roar of thunder break on top of us. Quickly the sky is aflame with lightning, the lake is rough and the rain is slashing down, almost as if a bucket has been overturned on to us.

Everyone, apart from Mum and I, makes a quick lurching exit to the saloon. One of the passengers slips down the stairs, her drink crashing to the ground. Mum and I can't stop laughing nervously as I make painful progress down the stairs. I am clinging on to her arm and the arm of a handsome German doctor. A supper tray skids past us turning upside down, tuna pasta salad falling on to the floor. 'I carry you?' he suggests, and before I have time to say no he picks me up, takes me down the stairs and awkwardly lands me on to one of the fold-up beds.

Lights are turned off. The German doctor waves goodnight to me as he settles on to his own bed with his girlfriend. It's only eight o'clock but there's nothing to do but lie in bed and dream of my own handsome doctor that I'm going to marry. And pray that my ankle will feel better tomorrow.

CHAPTER TWENTY-SEVEN

March 2000

'Dear Helen,

Seems like ages since you and James left. We're staying at Hwange safari lodge now. The first safari drive was dreadful. Our guide, Champion, was so desperate that he started pointing out chungalooloos, just to say something. They look like fat brown caterpillars. But the second night we saw a pride of lions. I think I counted thirteen. Mum insisted that there were fourteen but we didn't dare get out to count them. I can hardly make a quick escape. Well, I don't think any of us could. Ankle still v.sore.

Everyone out here is so friendly, just like you told me. Champion was great. He always helped me into the jeep and liked to push me in my wheelchair, zigzagging across the lawn down to the pool. The hotel is so empty – no tourists at all, just baboons everywhere – large ones, little ones, babies. One afternoon, when I was lazing by the pool, this big ugly baboon squatted on my reclining chair. It must have sneaked round the edge of the railings encircling the pool. You know what a wimp I am, I just snivelled, "Shoo, shoo, go away." It then reached out its long arm and nabbed all the packets of sugar, its teeth bared in a hideous grimace. Brave Diana ran at it with her John Grisham paperback. It did eventually go. There's supposed to be a man who keeps the baboons at bay. I've seen him in uniform and armed with a powerful catapult – but he's always asleep under the teak tree. Useless. Mum, Diana and I seem to be a constant source of entertainment. The night before poor Diana choked on a lump of steak and had to be saved by one of the guests on the next table. He was clutching her under the ribs and giving her sharp jerks, Diana burping and farting noisily. God, do you remember that time when I choked on a piece of stringy lettuce in that restaurant? It is terrifying. But you and I were given free puddings at least.

The Victoria Falls were incredible – even better than I had imagined. If I go again I will wear a bikini and not carry a neck purse with money in it. Mum and Diana took it in turns pushing me in the chair and when I stood up a waterfall cascaded down me. My money looked like soggy tissues.

I can't believe we are coming to the end of our holiday. Home in five days. I have no idea where I'm going to move to. Maybe some miraculous offer to live with Hugh Grant in Notting Hill will surface... what do you think?

Alice xxxxx

Ps. I have done some work for the book too... am not just lazing in the sun! Have read almost all of Granny's letters. All our conversations before we came out seem more real now. Her descriptions are so vivid in my mind. I'm reading the letters leading up to the war now.'

April 1939

More sleepless nights were spent listening to the wireless. Margaret and Gerald had bought the machine in 1935. It was large, about eighteen inches wide and at least two feet high. Gerald rigged up an aerial in one of the big trees. They were able to tune in to England, Paris, Berlin, Rome and a Dutch station. Gerald remembered vividly the first time he had listened to the news at home. He and Margaret had sat huddled together in eager anticipation. They heard some crackling and then saw a green light, like a big eye, followed by the sound of Big Ben striking. Margaret had burst into tears, saying she had never felt so close to England as she did now. They had bought it immediately for £34. However, a toy which used to give them so much joy was now an instrument of foreboding.

'Hitler is threatening peace again.'

'England fears rumours of war.'

'Hitler's menace grows.'

Gerald was the Chairman of the Farmers' Association and was planning the action of the district in case of war. Plans were being made for Margaret to stay at M'Coben with the children and other farming wives. Gerald had heard from the Coldstream H.Q. that he must be ready to be called up in the likely event of war.

It was late in the evening when Gerald wrote to his father. 'Our boys have served us for years, they are very devoted and loyal, and a certain pride in this place is growing up with them. They would look after Margaret, I'm sure.'

July 1939

It was becoming increasingly obvious that Hitler was determined to go to war. Gerald decided that the women needed to protect themselves as much as possible. He organised some shooting practice on one of the neighbour's farms, to teach them how to load and handle a revolver. Afterwards they would have to shoot five rounds.

'No, don't wave it about,' Gerald sighed to Margaret. 'Hold your arm still.' Margaret missed another target. 'The nerve in my elbow's playing up,' she complained. 'I'll shoot left-handed.'

Gerald moved on to the next person. 'How are you doing Mrs Mitchell?' he inquired hopefully.

'Jolly well I think.' She lined up and fired, missing completely.

'Excellent, but next time don't shut your eyes.'

1 September 1939
'Germany invades Poland.'

September 3
'Britain and France declare war on Germany.'

Plans were changed. Gerald was being kept in Rhodesia. The government had asked him to help train the Rhodesian battalion of the Black Watch. He decided not to let Margaret be on her own because it was impossible to know how long the war would last or what kind of propaganda Hitler would send down to Africa to stir up trouble. He organised for her to stay with Mrs Morris, the doctor's wife, and her family in Bulawayo. He was certain that Bulawayo was the best place for her. She would have no worries of native attacks, flooded roads, or being cut off from a doctor.

M'Coben would have to be closed down. The packing had started. Margaret had taken all the children's toys and clothes to Bulawayo. Linen, china and small pieces of furniture were being put into boxes. The cattle were going to be sold. Gerald hated the idea of breaking up the farm, but, he reasoned philosophically, it was a fate suffered by thousands of people everywhere. It was a price they had to pay when a war came.

He decided the best plan was to leave one boy in charge of their home. All he and Margaret could do was pray they would return one day.

George and Elardie were given their final pay packets, their faces dark and sad. Raden was going to be left in charge of the house while they were gone.

Margaret sat at the small wobbly table next to her bed writing her weekly letter home. She heard one of the doctor's children slamming a door. The walls were so thin that Margaret felt she couldn't breathe without being heard. She tried to stop herself from screaming as she wrote, 'The twins didn't like Bulawayo – the people, the noise, and the house and my life was hardly worth living. They howled all day and I felt like howling myself.'

She looked around the cramped room and longed to be back at M'Coben. Her home. 'I went back to the farm to pay off the boys and it looked so empty and sad. I could hardly bear it.' Margaret liked to go to the farm every week. However, each time she returned to Bulawayo it was with a heavy heart. M'Coben already looked derelict and uncared for. Like its name, Place of Ghosts. The day she had packed was the most heart-wrenching. Gerald, on the other hand, looked quite happy. 'I think he is revelling in being back in khaki and can see how much he is needed. I think he is looking forward to going back to England and seeing his old army friends.' Margaret put her head into her hands as she heard another unruly doctor's boy slam a door. 'I should be doing some kind of war work. I feel feeble for not doing anything – just the boring hum-drum jobs around this house. What am I going to do?'

Over the next few weeks Margaret found life hard. 'Gerald is so occupied training the recruits that I seldom see him and when I do we never have the opportunity to talk alone,' she wrote. 'I have had a row with Mrs Morris. She was storming around the house shouting and I told her in my cold husky voice, "I shall leave by the end of the week." She did apologise and I am still living with her as there is no other option. I am feeling increasingly isolated. The broadcast news is scanty and leaves so many gaps. I am steeling myself to the long separation and must do my best to be brave about it.' She was not only thinking about Gerald but Anne and Diana too. Bringing them back to Rhodesia seemed too dangerous, the fear of them being torpedoed too great a risk to take. Margaret had to admit to herself that they were better off at the Godolphin school in England. She was in agony over what to do herself. 'I long to return to England to be near the people I love and care about – but I feel it may be wrong.'

She told her mother that she was teaching the little girls how to cycle. 'They go off with Enoch, the nursery boy, at eight every morning to school. Patricia and Gill are not skilled cyclists. They have to be lifted on to their bicycles and then given a push. Just as they near school they shout, "Enoch, Enoch," and the kind boy has to cycle ahead of them, throw his bike on the ground and catch the children before they fall off!' Margaret smiled as she remembered watching them. 'I try not to think of life without Gerald. My little people are my saving grace.'

To Margaret's joy the doctor's family went to the Cape over Christmas. Margaret had the house to herself for the first time in months! She took the opportunity to entertain for a night, cooking dinner for friends before they went out for the evening. 'Gerald and I danced our feet off at the Grand Hotel and were pushed out at 1am. It was the best fun I'd had in ages.'

By the end of February, 1940, orders came through that the Rhodesian battalion must be ready for immediate overseas duty. Gerald was not sure where they were going but decided that Margaret should leave for England as soon as possible. He told her that she needed to be with her family. 'I am just not thinking about the uncertainties of the future – and praying England may be his destination and that we may all be together before too long.'

March 1940
Gerald and Margaret clung on to each other tightly. Margaret finally managed, 'Promise me you'll be safe. Promise me.'

Margaret and the children boarded the Bulawayo mail train. As the train began to move tears streamed down her face.

'I love you,' Gerald shouted, 'I love you!'

'I love you too,' Margaret shouted back.

Gerald ran alongside the train, he reached out to hold her hand one more time. And then he was gone.

CHAPTER TWENTY-EIGHT

25 March 1943, India
'My darling little rabbit,

I have such an intense longing to go home and see you that I frequently entertain secret hopes that I shall crack right up, so that I could be sent home with a clear conscience... Hitler's last speech was a very flat one, I thought, and not to be compared with Winston Churchill's. We are going to win the war all right, there is not a shadow of a doubt, but we are going to be mighty tired at the end of it. Well, I must stop as I feel I mustn't write any more in such a dreadful (in fact disgraceful strain!) but you needn't take it too seriously, as we, all of us, have to go through these woods. Hugs and kisses and squeeze all the children for me... Gerald.'

Entry in Margaret's diary, dated 11 March 1943
'Letter from Gerald. Rather depressed by the evening. Tired and sad and very lonely – Damn and Blast the War.'

'I listened to the wireless and prayed constantly,' Granny started, when I asked her about the beginning of the war. 'When I was at home with Mother I used to creep down late at night and listen to Lord Haw-Haw broadcasting German propaganda.'

'Why did you have to creep down?'

'Well, Mother would have been shocked.'

'Did Gerald's letters reach you?'

'Yes, but they were always out-of-date. Sometimes I went

266

three or four months without a letter or cable, and then I would receive a batch in one go. I would hear on the wireless snippets of information about where he was. One evening in April 1940, I learnt from the nine o'clock news that Gerald must have been in the Middle East, because it was announced that the Rhodesian battalion had disembarked at Suez. So that was that. I knew Gerald wasn't coming back to England.'

'Did you think he would die?'

'Yes, I always believed he would,' Granny confessed. 'I expected a telegram every day. Britain was in such danger too. By June 1940 Italy had joined Germany's side in the war. They had a large navy in the Mediterranean and troops in north and east Africa outnumbering the British by four to one.'

On 17 June 1940 the French Premier, Marshal Petain, asked for Armistice and Paris fell without a shot. Hitler expected Britain to surrender but we didn't. His next step was to smash the RAF and then invade. Although news reports weren't as comprehensive nor as sensationalised as they are today, most people would have known that Britain had its back to the wall. We were in a severely dangerous position.

'America was my saviour,' Granny told me. 'My brother Willie rang me in the middle of June 1940. "If I can get you there, will you take your children and mine to America?" he asked me. "There's a boat that sets sail in a week from Liverpool to Montreal. From there you can take the train to New York." He told me that my sister-in-law's American relations, the Phippses, had offered to maintain up to fifty children of their relations and friends.'

'How incredible,' I uttered. 'They must have been very well-off.'

'Yes, they were, but exceptionally generous with it. You know how sometimes the richest people can be the meanest. It was called the Phipps Blanket. I only had to think for a second or two,' Granny continued, '"Yes," I replied, "I'll go."' Granny had acted it out to me, nodding her head as if she were on the telephone that very moment. 'America was much safer for the children. So, I had a week in which to gather Willie's five children, Barty's two, the two elderly nannies – one of them was our devoted Nanny at Longford – and my six children before we set sail. Anne was sixteen and because she was old enough to work, she was allowed to come with me to help look after the twins. I had to gather both Anne and Diana from Godolphin school. I also had to organise visas and pass a fitness test at the American Embassy in London,' Granny recalled proudly. 'One of the boys, Reuben, was rather naughty and kept putting on a squint and a loopy expression when it came to his turn to have a medical. It was hideous. I never thought we'd leave. I wasn't allowed to take any money out of England.'

'You had no money at all?'

'I had a little for the journey. Gerald's parents travelled from Norfolk to say goodbye the night before I set sail. Gerald's mother, Mama, delved down her front and retrieved a little chamois leather bag. "You may need money, so sell this." Inside were all her many rings and other pieces of precious jewellery.'

'That's such a special thing to do.'

'I was touched. I wrote and told Gerald too, and I could see how much it meant to him. He was constantly worrying about how I was going to manage with so little money and indeed whether I would be able to get any out of the country.'

'How did Gerald feel about you going to America?'

'The funny thing was, he had no idea we were steaming off to America. He received my cable from Quebec three weeks late, so he finally heard in July, once we had arrived. Half the time we never knew where the other one was. I hadn't known he was in Somaliland until he returned safely.'

'Gerald would have been worried about the trip to America too, wouldn't he? I remember Mum telling me that the previous ship had been torpedoed.'

Granny nodded her head. 'Perhaps it was a mercy not to know what the other one was doing, we would have both been frantic with worry.'

'Did Gerald support you going to America?'

'Well, he was mightily relieved that we were all safe, that there was no danger the children and I would be bombed, that was always his main fear. Britain being invaded seemed a certainty at that time and we had no protection.'

'What was the journey like?'

'It was all right. Thankfully it lasted less than a week.'

Diana had told me the ship was overflowing with women and children. They were accompanied by warships and merchant navy ships. Two days after sailing they hit a storm which dispersed the whole convoy and blew them into the iceberg zone. Everyone was sick.

'Where did you stay?'

'To begin with we stayed at Westbury House which belonged to Aunt Dita and Uncle Jay. Aunt Dita was a formidable person with iron grey hair beautifully coiffed,' Granny described as she touched her own neatly curled grey-white hair, 'and she wore flowing silk dresses. She was very autocratic. She travelled around the gardens and grounds in a wonderful electric buggy accompanied by a fleet of yappy little dogs. Just like your dog, Jasmine. Her husband, Uncle Jay, was a small, red-faced man who always appeared to be in a hurry. Their house was lovely – beautiful gardens, a swimming pool, two full-sized polo grounds.'

As Granny described the house she reminded me of Audrey Hepburn describing the house and grounds of her home in the film, Sabrina Fair. 'What a change it must have been, especially as America was still a year and a half away from war,' I said.

'It was extraordinary. To begin with, I found it hard to adjust and felt I was dreaming or living in a film. I worried that I had done the right thing, that I hadn't gone mad and been swept away forever from all the people I loved back in England. At times I felt grateful I was safe. New York is a wonderful lively city, Alice. I'll always remember Gill's comment as we passed the World Fair Ground. She said, "This must be a very safe place, look at the lights!" You see, the whole of Britain was in black-out in 1940 so you can imagine the contrast. The children loved New York because they were taken out on shopping expeditions, were able to ride and watch polo matches. Then there were moments when I hated feeling so dependent upon other people and guilty at living in such luxury when people at home were enduring the hardships of war. The younger children had no idea of the danger Gerald was in and it was hard to believe that outside this protective shelter a war was going on.'

'How long did you stay at Westbury House?'

'Well, after six weeks at Westbury House my family were settled in a new home, Bonnie Blink, which stood on a hill with a fine view to the south of Long Island, eight miles from Westbury. Bonnie Blink housed six families. There were four mothers, two nannies and nineteen children!' she crowed incredulously.

'Had you heard from Gerald when you left for America?'

'There was still no news of Gerald when I left. The waiting was agonising.' She pressed her lips together. 'All I wanted to hear was whether he was dead or alive.'

'I can imagine,' I agreed, unable even to begin. 'How did you cope? How did you keep yourself sane?'

'It did help having Barty only a night's journey away from New York. Did I tell you he was stationed in Washington, involved in Military Intelligence work? He was a spy – and counter-spy operator. I looked forward more than anything to his occasional weekend visits. You see, even though the Americans were pro-British, I did at times feel isolated and alone, especially when there was constant bad news. It was grim,' Granny stressed, 'and I had to fight hard not to show my despair, especially in front of the children. Barty kept me going. I think I would have lost my senses if it hadn't been for him. I called him Saint Barty.'

'But what did you do with your time? The days of waiting for news must have been so long and drawn out?'

'Well, there was a lot to do – running the household, keeping the accounts, co-ordinating everything. I started a kindergarten for the small children at Bonnie Blink. Do you remember I told you about the Ozanne sisters? When I went to Paris before I married?'

'Yes, the finishing school.'

'That's right, well they came over to the States and Mlle

Alice used to come over to Bonnie Blink on two mornings to help me with my school. We taught the children to read, write, do simple sums, as well as learn French songs and games. Even the little twins joined in and started to learn their letters and paint numbers. It was a happy time, it certainly took my mind off Gerald for a part of the day. The other children were sent to schools, all paid for by the Phipps Blanket. I suggested to Aunt Dita that the children should go to state schools. She shrank back with horror. "But think who they might sit next to," she warbled.'

'No! I can't believe she said that.'

'I know, I did try to change her mind but she would not hear of it. In the end I gave in.'

'What else really stands out about your time at Bonnie Blink,' I asked.

'Feeling tired. I often lost my temper. You see the other mothers and I were so desperately worried about our husbands, thinking we had probably lost them. I remember the children playing the gramophone incessantly. Their favourite record was called, Hallelujah, I'm a bum. I remember one time feeling so cross and anxious about Gerald that I shouted, "If you don't turn that thing off I will SCREAM." "But Aunt Margaret, it's a HYMN," one of the children said back to me.'

'Did you get news from home?'

'I wrote to Mother regularly, that was always a comfort. I had hated leaving her in England. She wrote to me too but it was difficult to make out quite what was going on when the wireless reports were so dramatic, "London is on fire tonight! Will there be anything left by morning?"' She gasped at the memory.

I realised that she was referring to the Battle of Britain,

August to October 1940, when Hitler was trying to destroy Britain's air defences prior to invasion.

After the Battle of Britain disasters kept happening in quick succession. The main playing field of war moved to north and east Africa, Syria, the Mediterranean and Crete, which is precisely where Gerald was. He was in the battle for Crete, in May 1941, when the Germans invaded by parachute and desperate hand to hand fighting took place as the British defenders withdrew.

'When Gerald was in Crete, and I did know he was there,' she added, 'I was so hungry for news or some kind of reassurance, I even went to a fortune teller.' The anxiety was still loaded in her voice. 'Every day without a letter was like a part of me dying. I felt his life was sitting on a trigger, so to speak. I felt so powerless. All I could do was sit, wait and pray like I had never done before. I went to bed at night, tired but still unable to sleep.'

'Was the fortune teller able to give you any kind of reassurance?'

'None at all. She told me that I had had a conventional childhood. She mentioned nothing of Africa or Gerald. I think she was a terrible fraud. Alice, I can't tell you the overwhelming surge of joy I felt when I was called to the telephone by the Western Union Telegraph to hear the news that I had prayed so hard for: 'Safe and well after severe fighting.' I later received Gerald's letters from Crete in a batch, detailing the horrific fighting.'

15 June 1941
'We had a terrific fight on 20 May. After a three hours' "blitz"

by the Luftwaffe, which came over in hundreds, their troop carriers upset a battalion of parachutists right on top of us, in front of us and behind us. They dropped in right in front of my Company, which was dug in at the foot of a hill, overlooking a valley of small farms and vineyards. Several landed only a few yards away from my own trench and another officer and myself killed them all with hand-grenades. Altogether we had a desperate battle. My men were magnificent and soon the ground was strewn with corpses. Unfortunately we had fairly heavy casualties ourselves as the Germans shot down on us with Tommy guns from the air before they landed. Not only did they drop men on us, but also large containers, holding machine guns, mortars, ammunition etc but luckily most of these fell inside our wire entanglements. The Boche made desperate attempts to get at them and we killed scores of them as they crept up the vines in front of us on hands and knees trying to get at them... then a lot more were dropped further up our valley beyond our reach, and we were too occupied in our immediate vicinity to be able to do anything about them, and these people came down on us with a lot of machine guns and fired heavily at our positions. Then darkness came on and we heard the Germans calling out to each other all around us – gradually their voices withdrew into the night in front of us.'

'He fought very heavily in Tobruk, only six months after Crete,' Granny continued. 'Gerald was wrapped in excitement because it was the first time that his battalion were on the attack. You see, they were hanging on desperately at Crete and Somaliland, but this time they were in charge.'

9 December 1941

'At dawn, with a lot of tanks, and covered by our guns, we assembled in No Man's Land and then drove a deep but narrow wedge (just our battalion) right into the heart of the German defenses, from which they never recovered. We advanced nearly three miles, capturing several hundred prisoners and some guns, and very nearly a Brigade H.Q. which only escaped in time when a couple of Messerschmitts landed on the desert and took them off! But in doing this we were shot at from both flanks and in front by machine guns and artillery, and the price we paid was heavy... I am still very tired and upset at the loss of so many of my friends... but once more I have been amazingly lucky myself.'

'Granny, was there a tiny part of you that wished he wasn't fighting? Gerald was one of the oldest in his battalion, could he have stepped back and taken a less active role?' I asked.

'NO, no,' Granny exclaimed as if this was unthinkable. 'Gerald not fighting would not have been the Gerald I married. He had a tremendous sense of duty. He despised men who did not fight for their country. I remember him once being very angry when his parents suggested he could be given "leave". "There have been so few of us out here to defend the Empire that there can be no sitting back on anybody's part. England has got to fight like she has never fought before – or we are lost," he wrote to me. I knew he felt miserable leaving the family, he longed to be back at M'Coben. He loved it when I sent him snapshots of the children but he did also tell me they made him homesick. "It is difficult to realise that I haven't seen any of you for two years. The children all look so lovely,

I am so proud of them." But at the same time he was a soldier at heart and he was great friends with his battalion. It wasn't all fighting,' she insisted. 'They played golf and tennis. After Tobruk he was promoted to Major. I was so proud of him.'

'I don't understand how he managed to survive both Crete and Tobruk,' I said. 'I thought we were only given seven lives, Gerald appeared to have many more.'

'Well, he says it was because of his magic Cretan stick,' Granny smiled.

8 December 1941

'I have a wonderful stick, in which I have great faith. It is a magnificent thick shepherd's stick with a huge crook and was given to me by an old farmer in Crete, when a party of us passed through his village in the mountains on our way to the snows. He told me that it would bring me luck. I had it with me all through the invasion of Crete, and the other day when we attacked, I gripped it hard all the time when I fully expected to perish at any moment!'

'That's extraordinary. So Gerald must have had a very open mind, did he believe in alternative things?'

'Oh yes, apart from acupuncture. He didn't like the needles and it never worked for him,' she sniffed dismissively. 'A waste of time. Going back to Gerald, he was determined for Anne to go back to England to join the war effort. He felt everyone must do their part. I also joined the British Volunteer Movement Office which was full-time paid work in the consulate building in New York. I needed to be active otherwise I would have gone mad. I started work there in the middle of summer, 1942,' Granny recorded carefully. 'I had to gather up as many British Nationals as possible from all over the States and arrange for their transport to England. Letters from Gerald came quite regularly after that and I could see how exhausted he was getting. He hadn't had a single rest since the start of the war.'

'Where was he?'

'India. He joined the staff of the East Indian Army and was made Military Secretary. His headquarters were in Calcutta and the climate was suffocating, he was weary and tired. Gerald was forty-seven, much older than most serving soldiers so it was no shame. He was sent home in August 1943.'

'Tell me what it was like leaving America. You must have been so excited by the thought of seeing him! I don't think I could contain myself after four years apart.'

'I had to wait until I could get a passage back to England but by the time I settled on to the boat I was so excited I was almost popping. The journey was dangerous though, we had to carry life belts continuously, and I remember drinking sherry with the Captain and he told me we had passed through a pack of twenty U-boats. When I was finally on my way and felt we were safe, I was so happy to think that life might go back to normal again.'

December 1943

Margaret and the twins had left Bonnie Blink behind. They were travelling back to England as guests of the navy which had been arranged by her brothers in one of the new 'Woolworth carriers' built in America on the West Coast. The ship was made entirely of metal, even the curtain was a metal fabric. They were part of a large convoy consisting of six aircraft carriers, several destroyers and many other ships carrying American troops to England. The twins were five years old. Pam was plump with blonde curls, Richard slim with sandy-coloured hair. They could not look more different. Unlike Richard, Pam was not interested in learning and slow to read. 'I don't care, Richard will read to me,' she told Margaret. When Margaret encouraged Pam to learn how to tell the time she said, 'Richard will tell me.'

Barty had managed to get slightly later passages for Patricia, Gill and Diana on a Portuguese ship which took them to Lisbon. The girls would be safe on this ship as Portugal was a neutral country. Margaret was far more anxious about the plane they would catch from Lisbon to England. This journey posed a far greater risk – the Germans were in France. I cannot worry about it, Margaret told herself time and time again. They will fly safely to England and we shall all, finally, be reunited.

It was the last night on the boat and Margaret collapsed on to the bed, elated and full of eager anticipation for the next day. She felt like the young Margaret who used to return from the dances, her head still full of the music and the memories of dancing with Gerald. She remembered how she could never sleep after the dances. She was too excited about the next party and seeing Gerald again.

She picked up one of Gerald's last letters from her suitcase by her bed. They were packed neatly into a pile. She wanted to make sure she was not imagining how she felt. Could she allow herself to be this happy? Were they really going to be reunited?

'My darling little rabbit,

I sent you a wire two days ago, to say that I was going home. Isn't that wonderful, and I'm so excited I hardly know what to do!'

She read it over and over again. Finally her head hit the pillow, the walls were spinning. She was so happy! Quickly she fell into a deep sleep.

The following morning her head felt like a fuzz ball. For the first time in her life she knew what a real hangover was. She tried to get up to see to the twins and get a glass of water but her head was throbbing. She groaned with each creaky movement, images from the night before coming back to her. The wardroom hosts had set out to make her dead drunk, plying her with spirits and wine, mixed into brutal cocktails. How am I going to get the twins dressed and ready for disembarkation? she thought with horror. I can hardly get myself ready. They were expected to dock at Belfast. Then she had to get herself and the twins from there to Aberdeen.

She heard the steward coming to the door. 'Oh no, NO, I'm not ready,' she muttered as she stumbled out of bed, still in the same old crusty clothes from the night before.

'Sorry to say, milady, but orders are cancelled and we shall not reach port until tomorrow.'

To the steward's surprise Margaret beamed radiantly at him. 'Thank God!' she sighed as she flopped back on to the bed.

The next night Margaret tried not to drink despite her racing excitement. She wanted a clear head for the following morning.

She learnt that they were to dock at Greenock on the Clyde instead of Belfast.

Margaret caught a train to Glasgow. She had put on her best travelling suit, a dark jacket and skirt with a white blouse. She felt her hair. It hadn't changed in years, it was still in a short bob. Her skirt was loose, too much rushing around and looking after children was better than any diet. What would her Gerald look like? Would he look much older? He had told her in one of his letters that his moustache was beginning to go grey, 'with several white hairs just beneath my nose, but my head is still the same colour, I am glad to say!' She knew all of his letters off by heart.

Margaret shuffled her feet nervously. She was too restless to sit still. Pam and Richard were playing *I-spy*. What if he isn't there? she suddenly panicked. She had not imagined this horrific idea. Of course he will be waiting for me, don't be so silly, she cursed herself. It's the nerves getting the better of you, my dear, she could hear her mother tell her. Come on, train. Come on. Everything appeared to be going in slow motion. 'Richard, don't hit Pam,' she told him off. 'Calm down. You will see your father soon.'

'I don't know my Daddy,' Richard said.

'You will get on ever so well,' Margaret told him. 'Both of you. He adores you both. All his children are his pride and joy.'

Richard and Pam nodded blankly. Margaret could see they were excited but also could not quite comprehend the significance of today. How could they? Apart from the letters Gerald had written to his children, telling them where his quarters were, or the birds he had seen in India which were quite different to the African ones, describing the intense heat, and drawing pictures of what Italian warplanes looked like, he was no more than a shadow in their lives. Once they were together again it would be wonderful, everything would change.

After what seemed like an interminable train journey from Glasgow to Aberdeen the train ground to a halt and her hands trembled as the doors opened. The platform was crowded, figures emerging as the smoke cleared. She hardly dared look in case he wasn't there. She took a deep breath, it felt as if her stomach was in her mouth. Where is he? Where is he?

And then she saw a figure, standing tall, resplendent in his Black Watch kilt with the Black Watch insignia on it. He was still very slim but his blond hair was darker than she remembered.

She dropped her cases and ran towards him. Gerald's pace quickened. 'Is that Daddy?' Pam called after her.

Margaret did not have time to answer. She flung her arms around him. He stroked her hair as they hugged, Margaret staining his jacket with her tears.

Gerald picked up Richard and kissed him, then he picked up Pam and kissed her. He embraced Margaret again.

She had never thought he would survive and now, after four years apart, they were finally together again.

CHAPTER TWENTY-NINE

January 1944

Gerald was now in charge of all Home Guard activities in Aberdeen and was often out at nights and weekends. It was wonderful to be back together, but Margaret had noticed how much the war had taken out of him. His health had clearly deteriorated in the hot steamy climate. Despite his delight at seeing the twins, he found them too energetic. After everything he had been through all he wanted was some peace and quiet.

Diana, Patricia and Gill were staying in Pangbourne, near Reading, with Aunt Helen who was looking after them until the girls could travel up to Aberdeen. Gill was speaking to Gerald on the telephone. 'Daddy has a very English accent,' she told Helen after the call.

Patricia went on the line. 'You'll be seeing your father again,' Margaret said, 'he's very tired and you mustn't bother him too much. But he can't wait to see you.'

Diana, Patricia and Gill caught the train up to Scotland. As they stepped out on to the platform at Aberdeen, Patricia nudged Diana anxiously, 'I won't recognise Father. I don't know what he looks like.'

'It's all right,' Diana smiled as her step quickened towards the tall man with blond hair, 'just kiss whoever I kiss.'

'A very sad blow came in February 1944,' Granny stated. 'All our heavy luggage had been sunk in the Atlantic.'

'Oh Granny, I don't believe it.'

'I know. I had stocked up with shoes and clothing for the children before leaving the States, and the children's books and treasures were all lost.'

'What other memories do you have of Aberdeen?'

'It was very cold,' she laughed. 'We were living in a house in Abersnethick, overlooking the valley of the Don. We were two miles away from the local village shop but what with war rationing, my basket was never too heavy walking back home!'

'What sort of things were you able to buy?'

'Eggs and the occasional pot of honey were a real treat. I saved up sugar and in the summer I made jam with the wild raspberries. Gerald was allowed to fish on the river and he caught salmon and trout which made a delicious change to a rather boring diet.' She changes the subject. 'I remember enjoying the British spring, you see I had not seen one for four years. It was a joy to see the Don valley come to life – the fresh green foliage, the daffodils and primroses, the sheets of bluebells. It was magical.'

'Did you have a radio? Could you keep up with the war?'

'Oh yes, I had a small wireless. I listened to it every night while sewing. I heard the reports of the Normandy landings, of Mulberry Harbour, all the agonising fighting that went on. I shall never forget August 1945, VJ Day.'

'What is VJ day?' I asked.

'Victory Japan Day. You see, VE day was more greatly celebrated in Britain but in Aberdeen VJ day was of special significance. It was the home of the Gordon Highlander Regiment, and a large number were Japanese prisoners of war. I was on a bus with Anne and I caught the headlines of the man's newspaper next to me. 'Japan surrenders!' it said. The atmosphere was incredible, everyone cheering, waving, hugging each other as the news spread. Gerald and I knew in our hearts that we wanted to return to Africa, to our beloved home. However that night it didn't matter. We drank, we danced. We celebrated just life itself.'

CHAPTER THIRTY

During the last few days of our holiday I have reached the end of Margaret's letters to her mother from Africa. It must have been hard to know that when she returned to M'Coben she no longer had her weekly letter to look forward to. 'There is a blankness when your letter does not arrive, we just live for Thursday and all your home news,' she had written before the war.

It must have been even harder saying goodbye for the last time.

November 1945
'We are going back to M'Coben tomorrow Mother,' Margaret said as she sat quietly by her side at Homington.

Mother nodded. 'Your hair used to be so long. I remember Nanny putting it into curlers when you were little and you woke up with ringlets.' She was tired; each word summoned strength. Their conversation was disjointed, like a piece of a puzzle constantly being put in the wrong place.

'It's strange to think we're going back after nearly six years,' Margaret continued bravely. 'I promise to write to you the moment we arrive. I hope Raden and the boys will be there. It wouldn't be the same without them.' Margaret felt a large lump in her throat. She knew she had to change the subject otherwise she would cry. 'Do you know, I noticed that there were no towels on the ship!'

'I never wanted you to go to Africa,' Mother finally admitted, 'I was worried about you. Now I'm only proud.'

She looked at her daughter intently. 'I'm so proud of you,' she repeated as she closed her eyes.

'Goodbye my darling mother,' Margaret whispered as she was driven back through the thick fog to the boat in Southampton. She knew it had been their last meeting. She let herself cry as she heard her mother say again, 'I shall try to keep on writing to you. I loved your letters, I have kept every single one. They were a joy to me.'

I moved from my chair and sat next to Granny. 'Move over!' I told her. She made her familiar shrieking noise as she shifted her legs. I gently kissed her cheek as we hugged.

'I'm so glad she kept your letters. Otherwise we wouldn't be here now.'

'That's right,' she smiled.

I clutched her hand. 'I feel so lucky to know about your life.'

CHAPTER THIRTY-ONE

We are on the final stretch of our journey, driving back from Hwange safari lodge to M'Coben to say goodbye before returning home. I'm looking forward to seeing Granny's old home again. Mum and Diana find themselves still calling it their home too. It's a long journey – around a hundred and fifty miles. We are back on the familiar straight Bulawayo road. I sit quietly with my CD Walkman on, away in my own thoughts.

'Tell me what it was like driving back to M'Coben for the first time after the war ended,' I asked Granny as I turned on the dictaphone.

'It was wonderful,' she began. 'The only great sadness was that Gerald and Patricia were taken ill when we docked at Cape Town. Gerald was taken off the boat immediately as a stretcher case to the hospital, followed only hours later by my Patricia. Gerald had collapsed with a thrombosis; Patricia had what was like a tight boot string around her intestine.'

'What a nightmare!'

'Yes, a nightmare! I remember being on the verge of hysterical tears as I said to one of the doctors at the hospital, "You've just taken in my husband as a heart case, can you take Patricia too?" The idiotic doctor said she'd eaten too much ice-cream. It was much more serious than that because she was operated on that night, the surgeon removed the adhesion. I think she could have died,' Granny stated simply. 'Ten days later, when Patricia was taken off the danger list, I felt I could leave them both and make my own way to M'Coben to join the twins, Gill, Diana and Frances. I was picking the twins up from the neighbours on the way. The older girls were following on later.'

December 1945

As Margaret drove along the old track from Bulawayo, her heart felt as though it were in her stomach. Every corner and turn, each surrounding tree and bush, each pothole brought back memories. It was second nature to her. Margaret instinctively knew when to tell the children to hold on to each other as they went over rough patches in the road. She felt like a dog, the way they prick their ears and wag their tails as they sense they are near to home.

The car swooped down to the first bridge crossing the Umguza and Margaret had to accelerate to get up the other side. There had been a lot of rain, the river was swollen and raging. Margaret smiled at the familiar sight, thinking it felt as if she had never been away.

Margaret's palms were sweating against the wheel. She felt weak with anticipation. Are we doing the right thing returning? Margaret suddenly caught herself thinking again. Will we be able to make a success of M'Coben, earn enough money to support ourselves and the children? How much will Gerald be able to do? Are we insane to be coming back? We were so comfortable in England.

They reached the Mpandeni drift. 'We're nearly at M'Coben,' Margaret called to the twins. They looked blank. Margaret realised that none of these places – Bulawayo, Hilda's Kraal, M'Coben, meant a thing to them as they had only been a few months old when the war broke out.

Margaret knew that Mr Bingham had died during the war. Mrs Bingham, however, was still at Mpandeni running the house with a loyal native. Margaret breathed deeply. Thank goodness Mrs Bingham, who had always been her mother-figure, was still around. Would she be able to find George and Elardie? Would Raden still be at the house? Would their things still be there? Margaret was overjoyed that she had put in a claim to have power brought to M'Coben. That would make life a lot easier. Am I prepared for the hard work ahead? Margaret panicked again.

The road climbed and turned sharp left, then swung right to the approach to the house. It was too late to wonder if she was doing the right thing as M'Coben finally came into sight. The wheels churned across the track, the car making its way to the front of the house.

Margaret squinted as she tried to make out the figure waiting by the door. She knew that stance. It couldn't be, could it? She jumped out of the car and walked towards him, her heartbeat quickening with each step. As she drew closer she recognised the diamond-patterned tank-top.

'Hello Raden,' she said with an overwhelming urge to kiss him. Instead she shook his hand. Raden's eyes widened when he saw how tall the twins were. Margaret could almost hear him thinking, 'Are these the two babies I used to take for walks in the pram?!'

Pam shook Raden's hand. She was wearing a t-shirt, plimsolls and shorts to show off her long thin legs. Her hair was blonde and had changed from very curly to straight. Richard was also tall and slim, wearing khaki shorts and gym shoes. Raden shook his hand before turning to Margaret again. 'Welcome home Inkosikazi,' he beamed.

The house was dark and smelled musty. Margaret looked at the dressing-gowns, still hanging on the back of the bedroom doors. The beds were still made with the mosquito nets suspended from the rafters. She opened up the petrol box cupboards and stared in disbelief when she saw the white linen and blankets folded neatly next to each other.

When Margaret reached the sitting room she sat down and looked around her. Bushes were growing through the windows. Her feet brushed over the black and white chequered floor. She stared at the books lining the yellow shelves. She reached to the other side of the sofa and picked up the chintz cushion, holding it close to her. Gerald's desk, her desk on the opposite side, her sewing machine, the Longford picture hanging over the fireplace, even the zebras which Anne had made for her were all positioned just as they had been six years ago. Nothing had been moved. Nothing had been stolen! Margaret walked over to her desk, smoothing her hands over it. Every surface was caked in dust, forming smudged red patterns on her palms.

Margaret stepped out on to the verandah where she found the little table and wooden chairs ready for someone to make themselves comfortable. She felt like Sleeping Beauty awakening after one hundred years' absence. She could come in, make her bed and settle in straightaway. Surely there were not many places in the world where such a thing would be possible?

Raden interrupted Margaret's thoughts by telling her he had some tomatoes fruiting especially for her. She thanked him. 'It's wonderful to be back Raden.'

'Word of my return circulated like wildfire,' Granny said as she shifted her legs into a more comfortable position. 'The Africans came back to work, some having walked for miles, others travelling from as far afield as Nyasaland and Northern Rhodesia,' she explained. 'Elardie was one of the first to come back. He had worked for the Nyamandhlovu post office during the war. He had a wife and two little girls but he brought the sad news that George had died. I knew I would miss him greatly. George had been with us from the very beginning.'

'He made you that special macaroni with the crispy top,' I added.

'That's right, I had forgotten about that. I engaged another cook-boy called Sixpence but he was unpopular with the boys, especially Elardie. He would make these funny owl hooting noises outside the boys' huts. "There are spooks, ghosts, Raden wants to leave," Elardie told me. The thought of Raden leaving was so unbearable that I arranged for two spy boys to find out about these "spooks". They stayed up all night and caught Sixpence hooting and howling around the kraals to frighten the boys.'

I laughed. 'What did you do? Sack him?'

'I gave him a severe ticking off. I think he was jealous of Elardie and his young family because Sixpence was much older and had nothing.'

I feel that's a good enough reason. I am sure when I get older and still have no husband or children I shall start making howling noises. 'When did Patricia come home?'

'She returned from hospital in time for Christmas, saying she and Daddy had played many games of backgammon together.'

This sounded familiar as I can remember Patricia saying to me, "The first time I talked to my father without feeling scared of him was when we were both in hospital after crossing back to Africa. We played backgammon together and actually became friends."

'I had tried to keep the news of Patricia's emergency operation a secret from Gerald,' Granny confided, 'as I was terrified that it might upset his heart. It didn't work though, one of the nurses accidentally told him. Gerald didn't come home until March. I missed him, especially since my mother finally died that January, 1946,' Granny said sadly, as if the date was still firmly engraved in her mind. 'Still, I had to crack on, get the farm up and running again before Gerald returned.'

'How did you begin to get things going again?' I asked.

Granny told me she went to the authorities in charge of Fort Victoria prisoner-of-war camp and asked for two prisoners to help her rehabilitate the farm. 'They resented the fact that the boss was a woman. They did do a lot of the building work but started to get abusive and rude. I put them back on the train to the prison camp. I put in a claim for a three ton truck from the Army Disposal Depot. I also bought two more horses and a piebald black and white pony for Pam. I loved to ride before breakfast, but horses were also invaluable for riding round the farm and superintending the farm work. I bought some trek oxen and milking cows. I wanted us to be self-sufficient for dairy produce. Organised teams cleared and ploughed the land, mended fences and renovated buildings.

The roof had to be completely redone because the white ants had eaten into the thatch and damaged the timbers. Several of the door frames also had to be renewed because of the ants.'

'You are making me feel tired,' I said. 'What about your kitchen garden?'

'Oh yes, I got the vegetable garden back in production. By the new year fifty acres had been cleared and ploughed for planting maize,' Granny continued, 'and miraculously the windmill was still in working order and water ran from the bathroom taps. It didn't take long to get back to normal again. My incentive was Gerald. I didn't want him to worry about a thing. I wanted everything to be perfect on his return.'

March 1946

Margaret could not find any of the boys or the children. The children were back from school for the holidays. Patricia and Gill were at a boarding school in Salisbury. Richard was at a prep school in Ruzawi near Marandellas. Diana was starting her first year at Cape Town University. Anne was with them for a few months before returning to England to attend the Camberwell School of Art in London. Pam was the only one who stayed at M'Coben. Margaret had enrolled her on a correspondence course so as to keep at least one child at home for company.

Margaret finally heard lots of laughter behind the chicken house. N'dende, the deaf and dumb farm boy who now helped Margaret with the chickens, was marching up and down, brushing his pretend moustache and twiddling his walking stick. To Margaret's surprise everyone was finding this hilariously funny. When N'dende started to strut up and down, ordering everyone around, wearing a felt hat and holding pretend keys, the boys were on the ground with laughter. Elardie turned round and saw the Inkosikazi. At once they stopped, shame-faced. 'No, carry on,' Margaret waved her arms, realising that N'dende was performing a cabaret of her and Gerald. 'But don't do it when Inkosi[1] is here. He's coming home tomorrow and we're going to have a party!'

Margaret could not wait for tonight. The farm was buzzing with excitement, Elardie and the boys had invited all their friends to the party to celebrate the Inkosi's return. The women had been busy brewing beer in great drums over a fire at the farm buildings, ready for the big occasion.

For the first time in months Margaret slipped out of her working dungarees, leaving the belt and heavy keys she normally carried around her waist on the back of her chair. She put on a flowered dress and a straw hat with a navy ribbon tied around it. Gerald stood behind her and tied the clasp of her pearl necklace. She turned to thank him. He looked a picture in his kilt and cap with a smart shirt and tie. He looked so handsome. She must take a camera tonight, she thought.

Gerald, Margaret and the children, each wearing colourful cotton or straw hats, made their way to the party. It was won-derful for the whole family to be together after such a long time. Margaret walked next to Anne, who was now taller than her and twenty years old. Margaret found it hard to believe she was so grown up. Everyone assembled around the family. The Africans were wearing their smartest trousers, shorts and shirts. Some of the boys wore caps. The girls wore checked dresses and kerchiefs in their hair. The young children looked

---

[1] The king

294

curiously at Gerald, the older ones shook his hand. He was touched to see so many old faces as he clapped the backs of Elardie, Raden, N'dende and James the head farm boy. His faith in their loyalty had not been misplaced. They had come to see M'Coben as their home, he thought with pride, almost as much as his own family had.

The Africans danced for the family. They sang and played the drums and stamped their feet triumphantly. Elardie came forward and magically calmed the noise down. He turned to Gerald. 'We are happy you have returned,' he said. 'We have missed you and we welcome you back home.'

Gerald cleared his throat and tears sprang to his eyes. 'Thank you Elardie. Thank you to all of you for looking after our home. I've dreamed about this moment for a long time and it's wonderful to be back!' Everyone drank and cheered. 'The Inkosi wears a skirt, the Inkosikazi wears the trousers!' shouted Elardie.

Margaret watched Gerald smile broadly at the boys. She took a photograph. Tonight made everything worth it. The anxiety, the loneliness, the pain of separation had gone. Margaret seized his hands and pulled him to his feet. 'Dance with me, darling,' she said.

As Gerald turned with Margaret, he spoke softly into her ear, 'We did the right thing coming back.'

CHAPTER THIRTY-TWO

March 2000

We have been staying with Fred and Betty for two nights and are about to make the long journey back to Harare. Our final night will be spent with the Piercys where we stayed when we first arrived.

The news has been deteriorating steadily over the past few days. We are anxious about the petrol shortage and are planning to go to the Europcar depot in Bulawayo to ask for their help. It's a six-hour journey from Bulawayo to Harare. We're going to need a full tank of petrol.

However the petrol shortage is only one of the severe problems. Despite Mugabe being defeated in the February referendum – the first opposition victory in any vote since independence – he remains undaunted, clinging on to his power any way he can.

Mugabe is still threatening to seize white-owned farms. Betty showed us a comprehensive list drawn up by the National Farmers' Union, naming all the owners of farms in Zimbabwe who had been earmarked for take-over. I scanned the list and was relieved not to see M'Coben and Spring Grange, nor the Piercys' home. But Betty reminded me that this probably wasn't fool-proof. If invasions were to go ahead would the invaders follow such a list? 'Nothing is predictable in this country,' she said.

'Is there anything the police can do?' I asked.

Fred immediately smiled. 'My dear, you have never lived in a country where the rule of law does not exist.'

The car is packed and we are finally ready to go. We say good-bye to Paul, Mathanda, Regina and Ambrose. Ambrose has cleaned our car and it is shining as if it is the star prize on a game show.

Don't let me cry, I think as I hug Fred. Over his shoulder I see something marbled. 'What's that?' I quaver, pointing to the ground. Fred moves out of the way. Dad veers away. He is worse than me. Mum told me that when they went out for walks he followed her every footstep, just as Aunt Mildred had with Gerald. One time Dad walked back to the house, very despondent, saying Mum and Diana had sent him home because they wanted to go for a proper walk.

'It looks pretty dead to me,' Diana observes.

'No, it's not, I saw it's tongue flicking in and out,' I murmur, stiff with fear. There is a marbled grey snake within inches of my toes.

'I'm sure it's still alive,' Dad echoes.

Fred, Betty and Mum are standing close together. 'I fished it out of the dustbin,' Fred whispers to Mum, 'I found it under the sofa days ago. I was longing for Alice to see one. Don't tell her.'

We say goodbye to M'Coben, Place of Ghosts, each one of us quiet in our own thoughts. As I look at Mum and Diana I know that they are thinking it is the last time they will see their old home.

As we approach Bulawayo our thoughts momentarily divert from Betty and Fred to petrol. The queue outside the petrol station is like a long snake of traffic, twisting and turning around many different corners. I can't see the end of it. We have no luck at the Europcar office and there is nothing for it but to join in the crawling line of cars.

'Get to the fucking end of the queue,' a dark-haired man bellows, thumping the window of our car with an angry fist. That would be easy if we knew where it was. Eventually we are sent off in the right direction.

Two hours later we reach the top of the queue. I am dreading the supply running out just as we approach the pumps. This petrol crisis has been going on for a few months now. Back in December, before coming out to Africa, we were warned by many people that we might not get petrol. When we first arrived at the Piercys, six weeks ago, they were having terrible problems getting diesel for their boat. Their business was drying up because of the petrol crisis. It's OK, the man is beckoning us towards the first pump. Phew.

We arrive at the Piercys at eight that evening. It was terrifying driving in the dark. Dad and Diana couldn't work out how to adjust the car headlights and I couldn't reach the buttons because I was stuck rigidly between two suitcases. There was nowhere to stop either. 'There's a pedestrian on the road,' Dad shouted. We swerved in front of oncoming traffic, sank into potholes and missed all the right turnings. I feel sure someone 'up there' was looking after us as we didn't hit anything. We are given large drinks, Diana goes up to have a bath, muttering under her breath to me that she is sure she smells. Our drive is quickly forgotten when the Piercys tell us the news that we have been dreading.

The farm invasions have begun.

'I know this sounds stupid,' I tell Dad as we leave after saying all our final goodbyes, 'but I want them to come home with us. Fred, Betty, Peter, Barbara, all of them. I don't want to leave them here.'

'It doesn't sound stupid,' Dad assures me. 'The trouble is, they don't want to come.'

The Piercys' staff stand waving their arms as we leave. We understand our popularity. By mistake we tipped them about five times as much as we should have done the first time we stayed. But who cares? I don't.

Just before our car turns the corner, I twist round and wave back at the smiling line of faces for the final time.

CHAPTER THIRTY-THREE

April 2000

I'm back at home. Being in Africa seems little more than a distant dream.

Granny is staying with us. She has told Mum and me repeatedly how relieved she is to have us home. Unable to think about what is happening in Zimbabwe, she asks me how the writing is going. 'Have you nearly finished the book now?'

'Nearly, Granny.'

'You must crack on with it,' she says sternly. 'You must have written about the time just after we got electricity on the farm when one of the boys thought that he had been bitten by a snake. I was supposed to inject between the wound and the heart but the man was so thin that I plunged the needle into his bottom. The following morning he felt much better, it had probably been a scorpion bite. The doctor told me that I could have done real damage by giving him the anti-snake inoculation. I could have lamed him for life.'

'No, I haven't put that in, although it's a great story Granny. It must have been wonderful to have electricity after the war.'

'It was a joy. We had the whole house and all the out-buildings wired up, and we took power down to the farm buildings too so we could install a proper food mill. Did you write about the boy who thought he was a bird and climbed up the electricity pole and swung on to the line? He was given an almighty jolt of electricity but luckily managed to tumble back on to the ground.'

'I like that story,' I say as I scribble it down.

'Or the time when Patricia and I could not get back over the river so had to swim with our shopping bags and hand-bags around our necks?'

'No,' I squeeze out, feeling a great failure.

'I think one of the best stories is when we saw a swarm of locusts. Gill kept on tugging at my sleeve and I was so preoccupied with getting rid of the wretched locusts that I ignored her, until I saw she had stuck a peanut up her nose. I had to rush her into hospital. You must have written about that?'

'Sorry.'

'What have you written about then?'

I take a deep breath. 'Everything we've talked about in our sessions, Granny. The workers, George, Elardie and Raden.'

Granny smiles when I say their names. 'They were my favourites,' she admits, 'they were so loyal.'

'The story ends when you return to the farm after the war.'

Granny sits up abruptly. 'You must write about the farm after the war, that's when we were so successful. You must put something in,' she insists. 'I grew all sorts of vegetables for the Bulawayo market which paid very well. We put down a bore-hole and installed an electric pump. I irrigated a plot below the house and planted onions, cabbages, cauliflowers.' Proudly she adds, 'It was my own invention.' Granny clicks her teeth. 'The dairy was also jolly successful. The Red Poll herd was back in production and we were sending cream to the Bulawayo creamery three times a week.'

As I watch Granny talk so animatedly I can see why she wanted me to go on. Gerald and Margaret never made any money before the war. However, after the war, farming enjoyed great prosperity, and M'Coben became very successful. Everything they had worked towards finally came to life. To cut it short would be like abruptly stopping a couple kiss at the end of a film when they had overcome so many obstacles to be together.

'We grew Indian hemp because the seed was in demand as a green manure crop for the tobacco plantations in Mashonaland,' Granny continued. 'Gerald devised the idea that if we grew kaffir-corn-millet instead of maize, we could reap it with a combine harvester. We went ahead and bought a tractor and a Massey-Harris combine harvester. It was wonderful. We had some four hundred acres cleared and ready for cultivation.'

'I will write all of that,' I reassured her.

'You must. We grew cotton every year too. Gerald and I were put on to the Cotton Board which met at Gatooma where the main spinning mills were. That was our main crop. It was picked by hand and all the womenfolk helped, we paid them by weight but I had to make them empty the sacks because they would put heavy stones in the bags to bolster the weight.'

'You always had to be alert didn't you?'

'Always. I also learnt that there was a good market for eggs so decided to go in for chickens. We built chicken houses made out of sun-dried bricks and the deaf and dumb boy, N'Dende, looked after them. We managed to communicate through wonderfully lively signs and he loved to mimic Gerald and me!'

'I've put that story in,' I tell her.

'Gradually through the years we built up a flock of 1,500 laying fowls. Did you mention that I was involved in WI work after the war?'

'Yes,' I pretend.

'Oh good, because I was the President, you know. In 1950 I was elected National Chairman of the WI and I had to meet every WI member in Rhodesia. When we left for England, I was presented with a gold brooch, the Rhodesian lily.'

Granny wears her Rhodesian lily every day. I tell her that we met one of her WI contemporaries, Kay Hawkins, when we were in Africa.

'I know,' Granny nods, 'Diana told me she was rather thin, three quarters blind, terribly immobile but a terrific chatterer.' It's funny the way Granny is competitive about her contemporaries. She is proud not to be as immobile and emaciated as they are. She recently told me how incontinent one of her old Norfolk friends was. I felt I ought to be handing her the 'I'm not incontinent' trophy. She does it with me too. She loves to offer me the more comfortable chair in the corner of the kitchen. It's a will to be stronger than others. It's very powerful and ultimately I think it keeps her going.

'Why did you leave Africa Granny?' Gerald and Margaret left in 1953. 'You seemed so happy there.'

'We were,' Granny acknowledges, 'but the altitude was affecting Gerald. Remember, Anne, Diana and Gill were now married and all in England. Patricia lived in London. We wanted to be near our family. Gerald bought about seventy acres of the Witchingham estate. You remember The Warren don't you?'

'Yes, of course I do. I loved going to Norfolk. I remember

the sunken boat,' I smile. 'I remember the smell of the bracken, the woods and the river.'

'That's right,' Granny nods, 'Gerald bought the whole Great Witchingham stretch of the River Wensum. We were happy in Norfolk. It was a wrench to leave M'Coben, especially Raden and Elardie who were like family, but all good things have to come to an end. I think it was time to go.'

CHAPTER THIRTY-FOUR

BBC News, 2000
'Martin Olds, a vocal member of the farming community, was murdered on 18 April 2000. He was alone in the family farmhouse at Nyamandhlovu, three hundred miles south of Harare, when about one hundred self-styled war veterans turned up to take over the land. He had received death threats and one white farmer had already been killed.'

'The police did not react.'

February 2001
Since being home, for the past nine months we have heard sporadic news from Peter, Barbara, Fred and Betty. Peter wrote a long account of what life had been like during the nine months after we had gone.

'For Zimbabwe, the Millennium will be recorded as the infamous Land Grab, when murder and mayhem was the norm on many farms, carried out by so-called War Veterans and supported by Government organs such as the Police. This campaign of terror was directed against white farmers only, and included all their workers, who suffered the most in physical terms, as well as seeing their homes torched and losing all their meagre possessions.

Martin Olds' death was met with shock, horror and total disbelief that such an event was remotely conceivable in our civilised society. Farmers and their families throughout Matabeleland vacated their farms and took refuge wherever they could in Bulawayo to see what would happen next. But it was an isolated event which made it all the more inexplicable. Those of us who knew Martin Olds also knew of his hot-headed bravery, the sort that wins V.C's. After all Mugabe gave him a medal for rescuing a man literally from the jaws of a crocodile.

During May nearly all of us filtered back to our farms to try and pick up the normal threads of life again, though normal life was a bigger bunch of keys, with ever more padlocks in strategic places, and a radio network connecting all the farmers in each rural district. Our first farm invasion was a weekday, 25 May. Eight to ten men demanded to speak to me. I suggested three was enough, but they all pushed in as I unlocked the gate, and this alone sparked off my irritation, so that I stopped halfway to the farm office and demanded to know their ages and pointed to each man individually. I think they were caught short in surprise, and so we went through this roll-call, except for one young boy who remained silent. I hoped at least that I had given the impression of my total unconcern, whilst inwardly my mind, and my stomach too, were churning with nervousness.

In the following six months we talked of little other than how much of the farm they were going to take, whilst I attempted to explain why I would concede nothing. Whatever solid facts of farm productivity and labour welfare I trotted out, these were met with the bland reply the farm was theirs now. I tried to elicit a response to such questions as why we all suffered from the fuel shortage, why there were no tourists, why unemployment had increased. Such revelations made one or two somewhat thoughtful, but in the main it was a waste of breath. Some of them admitted they had been resettled on State-acquired land in the previous fifteen years, to which I would retort that NOBODY HAD GIVEN US ANYTHING, BUT THAT IT HAD TAKEN US NINETEEN YEARS TO REPAY OUR DEBTS.

It was always essential to try to identify leaders of each deputation and to try to limit the numbers to a few for some discussion, and as different deputations of these war-lords (as we called them) arrived, we would pretend huge amusement that they were all trespassing on each other's territory. Just a few would actually apologise and depart. On other occasions people arrived in dribs and drabs as well as dozens and we would learn that some other war-lord in Bulawayo had charged them $40 for their patch on the farm! Most would realise how they had been tricked and depart, but inevitably, like a stain from spilt liquid, a few would try to establish themselves and start to build a hut, but as this is being written nine months later, there has been no intrusion or occupation of permanence here.

We have had to employ six farm guards who roam at will anywhere on the farm and report back, or are sent to investigate any suspicious event. The message that comes back is always the same: our visitors refuse to talk to the guards, they insist on talking to the BOSS. I have usually gone with one escort, a farm worker, mainly for translation purposes, but also as a witness to the proceedings. I believe it does help to meet face-to-face and be willing to discuss. I try to introduce social conversation – such as numbers in his family, children, his previous employment, his Fifth Brigade experiences (a winner!) so that even when a 'Mahomet and mountain' situation is evident, each is aware of the other's standpoint. If I was aggressive I only think that would lead to a violent outcome. When aggression is automatically anticipated, sweet reasonableness can be disarming.

Dependent upon your personality and sensitivity, we each live day by day between worry and fear, uncertainty and despair. Unsure just where to draw the fine line between sticking to principles or compromising to save one's skin. The boxer weaves and ducks to avoid punishment while he tries for the knockout blow, in the knowledge the referee is impartial. It is not so here, and I must learn to hide my frustrations, swallow my pride, and adopt flexible principles like a street-wise politician. While I am not brave enough to be a martyr as have the six farmers murdered in this Land Grab era, I like the saying, 'If good people do nothing, evil will prevail.' I am lucky I have not suffered the injury and trauma that many fellow farmers have suffered to put me to the test.'

I read the letter to Granny and she sits still and quietly, absorbing every word. She's been following the news in Zimbabwe religiously but wants to hear it first hand. After a long pause, she finally says, 'You certainly went out at a troubled time, I'm still so relieved you're back safely. Any later and you would not have been able to go.'

I agree. If our flight had been booked in February of last year, rather than January, it would have been a very different holiday by the end. We had left with fear for all the new friends we had made and a feeling of profound wonder that we had spent six memorable weeks, encountering nothing but kind helpful people from white and black alike, 'at a time when the country was sliding into the abyss,' as Diana said.

'It's Peter's home, they have nowhere else to go. I wish all Africans, whether black or white could live and work together again,' Granny sighs. 'We were all blissfully happy at M'Coben. We have so much to give each other. It won't happen in my lifetime, I'm afraid. All I can do is pray that it will happen in yours.'

Granny closes her eyes. I realise now just how many memories she has to hold on to. She only has to shut her eyes to step back in time and hear Gerald's voice. To see him smoking his pipe and reading to the children on the verandah. Or eating his favourite cherry cake. I imagine she is now taking herself back to the camp fire that very first night when they sat under the stars and George made them macaroni cheese with a crispy top. I am sure she can still feel the warmth of the fire and Gerald sitting close to her.

A Reading from Revelation: 21, vv 1–4.

And I saw a new heaven and a new earth; for the first heaven and the first earth were passed away; and there was no more sea.

And I, John, saw the holy city, new Jerusalem, coming down from God out of heaven, prepared as a bride adorned for her husband.

And I heard a great voice out of heaven saying, Behold, the tabernacle of God is with men, and he will dwell with them, and they shall be his people, and God himself shall be with them, and be their God.

And God shall wipe away all tears from their eyes; and there shall be no more death, neither sorrow, nor crying, neither shall there be any more pain: for the former things are passed away.